AQA

Biology A

Student Workbook

Model Answers: 2009

This model answer book is a companion publication to provide answers for the exercises in the **AQA Biology AS Student Workbook** 2009 edition. These answers have been produced as a separate publication to keep the cost of the workbook itself to a minimum, as well as to prevent easy access to the answers by students. In most cases, simply the answer is given with no working or calculations described. A few, however, have been provided with more detail because of their difficult nature.

www.biozone.co.uk

ISBN 978-1-877462-19-1

Copyright © 2008 Richard Allan
Published by BIOZONE International Ltd

 BIOZONE

Additional copies of this Model Answers book may be purchased directly from the publisher

EUROPE & MIDDLE EAST:
BIOZONE Learning Media (UK) Ltd
P.O. Box 23698, Edinburgh
EH5 2WX, Scotland
Telephone: 131-557-5060
FAX: 131-557-5030
E-mail: sales@biozone.co.uk

ASIA & AUSTRALIA:
BIOZONE Learning Media Australia
P.O. Box 7523,
GCMC 4217 QLD, Australia
Telephone: +61 7-5575-4615
FAX: +61 7-5572-0161
E-mail: sales@biozone.com.au

NORTH & SOUTH AMERICA, AFRICA:
BIOZONE International Ltd
P.O. Box 13-034,
Hamilton, New Zealand
Telephone: +64 7-856-8104
FAX: +64 7-856-9243
FREE FAX: 1-800-717-8751(USA/Canada only)
E-mail: sales@biozone.co.nz

Contents

Contents

Contents

Hypotheses and Predictions (page 15)

1. Prediction: Woodlice are more likely to be found in moist habitats than in dry habitats.

2. (a) **Bacterial cultures**:
   Prediction: Bacterial strain A will grow more rapidly at 37°C than at room temperature (19°C).
   Outline of the investigation: Set up agar plates of bacterial strain A, using the streak plating method. Place 4 plates in a 37°C incubator and 4 on the lab bench. Leave all 8 plates for the same length of time (e.g. 24 hours), with all other conditions identical. Measure the coverage of the agar plates with bacteria (as a percentage).
   (b) **Plant cloning**:
   Prediction: A greater concentration of hormone A increases the rate of root growth in plant A.
   Outline of the investigation: Set up 6 agar plates infused with increasing concentrations of hormone A (e.g. 1 mgl^{-1}, 5 mgl^{-1}, 10 mgl^{-1}, 50 mgl^{-1}, 100 mgl^{-1}, 500 mgl^{-1}), and each plate with 12 clones of plant A. Measure root length each day for 20 days.

Planning an Investigation (page 17)

1. Aim: To investigate the effect of temperature on the rate of catalase activity.

2. Hypothesis: The rate of catalase activity is dependent on temperature.

3. (a) Independent variable: Temperature.
   (b) Values: 10-60°C in uneven steps: 10°C, 20°C, 30°C, 60°C.
   (c) Unit: °C
   (d) Equipment: A means to maintain the test-tubes at the set temperatures, e.g. water baths. Equilibrate all reactants to the required temperatures in each case, before adding enzyme to the reaction tubes.

4. (a) Dependent variable: Height of oxygen bubbles.
   (b) Unit: mm
   (c) Equipment: Ruler; place vertically alongside the tube and read off the height (directly facing).

5. (a) Each temperature represents a treatment.
   (b) No. of tubes at each temperature = 2
   (c) Sample size: for each treatment = 2
   (d) Times the investigation repeated = 3

6. It would have been desirable to have had an extra tube with no enzyme to determine whether or not any oxygen was produced in the absence of enzyme.

7. Variables that might have been controlled (a-c):
   (a) Catalase from the same batch source and with the same storage history. Likewise for the H_2O_2. Storage and batch history can be determined.
   (b) Equipment of the same type and size (i.e. using test-tubes of the same dimensions, as well as volume). This could be checked before starting.
   (c) Same person doing the measurements of height each time. This should be decided beforehand.

   Note that some variables were controlled: The test-tube volume, and the volume of each reactant. Control of measurement error is probably the most important after these considerations.

8. Controlled variables should be monitored carefully to ensure that the only variable that changes between treatments (apart from the biological response) is the independent (manipulated) variable.

Experimental Method (page 19)

1. Increasing the sample size is the best way to take account of natural variability. In the example described, this would be increasing the number of plants per treatment. **Note**: Repeating the entire experiment as separate trials (as described) is a compromise, usually necessitated by a lack of equipment and other resources. It is not as good as increasing the sample size in one experiment run at the same time, but it is better than just the single run of a small sample size.

2. If all possible variables except the one of interest are kept constant, then you can be more sure that any changes you observe in your experiment (i.e. differences between experimental treatments) are just the result of changes in the variable of interest.

3. Only single plants were grown in each pot to exclude the confounding effects of competition between plants (this would occur if plants were grown together).

4. Physical layout can affect the outcome of experimental treatments, especially those involving growth responses in plants. For example, the physical conditions might vary considerably with different placements along a lab bench (near the window vs central). Arranging treatments to minimise these effects is desirable.

   Checklist to be completed by the student.

Recording Results (page 21)

1. See the results table at the top of the next page.

2. The table would be three times as big in the vertical dimension; the layout of the top of the table would be unchanged. The increased vertical height of the table would accommodate the different ranges of the independent variable (full light, as in question 1, but also half light, and low light. These ranges would have measured (quantified) values attached to them.

Variables and Data (page 22)

1. (a) Leaf shape: **Qualitative**
   (b) Number per litter: **Quantitative**, discontinuous
   (c) Fish length: **Quantitative**, continuous.

2. Quantitative data are more easily analysed in a meaningful way, using descriptive and inferential statistics. Statistical tests are often required to properly test a hypothesis. **Note**: Qualitative data can be tested statistically but the tests are very complex and generally not very powerful (their ability to detect differences between data sets is sometimes limited).

3. Measure wavelength (in nm) with a spectrophotometer; which measures light intensity as a function of the colour, or more specifically, the wavelength of light.

4. (a) Many variables could be chosen. Examples include: gender, viability (dead or alive), species, presence or absence of a feature, flower colour. These data are categorical; no numerical value can be assigned to them.
   (b) These data are semi-quantitative because

		Trial 1 / CO₂ conc. in ppm											Trial 2 / CO₂ conc. in ppm											Trial 3 / CO₂ conc. in ppm										
		Minutes											Minutes											Minutes											
	Set up no.	0	1	2	3	4	5	6	7	8	9	10	0	1	2	3	4	5	6	7	8	9	10	0	1	2	3	4	5	6	7	8	9	10
Full light conditions	1																																		
	2																																		
	3																																		
	Av.																																		

arbitrary numerical values have been assigned to a qualitative scale. The numbers are correct in a relative sense, but do not necessarily indicate the true quantitative values.

Transforming Raw Data (page 23)

1. (a) Transforming data involves performing calculations using the raw data to determine such properties as rates, percentages, and totals.
   (b) The purpose of data transformation is to convert raw data into a more useful form.

2. (a) **Transformation**: Percentage (percentage cover)
   Reason: Abundance alone might not reflect the importance of a species in terms of its dominance in the habitat.
   (b) **Transformation**: Relative value (ml per unit weight)
   Reason: this transformation allows animals of different body size to be compared meaningfully without the interfering influence of actual body size.
   (c) **Transformation**: Reciprocal
   Reason: Provides a measure of rate where the data have been recorded over very different time periods (time taken for precipitation to occur). It is difficult to compare values where the time scale is different for each recording.
   (d) **Transformation**: Rate
   Reason: Data may have been recorded over different time periods. A rate allows the production of CO_2 to be compared per unit of time over all temperatures (removes the confounding effect of different time periods as well as different temperatures).

3. Performing data transformations:
   (a) Incidence of cyanogenic clover in different regions:

Clover type	Frost free No.	%	Frost prone No.	%	Totals
Cyanogenic	124	78	26	18	150
Acyanogenic	35	22	115	82	150
Total	159	100	141	100	300

   (b) Plant transpiration loss:

Time/ min	Pipette arm reading/ cm³	Plant water loss/ cm³ min⁻¹
0	9.0	-
5	8.0	0.20
10	7.2	0.16
15	6.2	0.20
20	4.9	0.26

(c) Photosynthetic rate at different light intensities:

Light intensity/ %	Average time/ min	Reciprocal of time/ min⁻¹
100	15	0.067
50	25	0.040
25	50	0.020
11	93	0.011
6	187	0.005

(d) Frequency of size classes of eels:

Size class/ mm	Frequency	Relative frequency/ %
0-50	7	2.6
50-99	23	8.5
100-149	59	21.9
150-199	98	36.3
200-249	50	18.5
250-299	30	11.1
300-349	3	1.1
Total	**270**	**100.0**

Data Presentation (page 25)

1. The difference between the two means (labelled A) is not significant, i.e. the two means are not significantly different because the 95% CIs overlap. The mean at 4 g m⁻³ has such a large 95% CI we cannot be confident that it is significantly different from the mean at 3 g m⁻³ with the very small 95% CI.

2. Graphs and tables provide different ways of presenting information and each performs a different role. Tables summarise raw data, show any data transformations, descriptive statistics, and results of statistical tests. They provide access to an **accurate** record of the data values (raw or calculated), which may not be easily obtained from a graph. Graphs present information in a way that makes any trends or relationships in the data apparent. Both are valuable for different reasons. **Note**: Even when you have calculated descriptive statistics for your data and tabulated these for the reader, it is a good idea to include your raw results as an appendix, or at least have them available for scrutiny.

Drawing Bar Graphs (page 26)

1. (a) Table as below:

Species	Site 1	Site 2
Ornate limpet	21	30
Radiate limpet	6	34
Limpet sp. A	38	-
Limpet sp. B	57	39
Limpet sp. C	-	2
Catseye	6	2
Topshell	2	4
Chiton	1	3

(b) Bar graph: *See next page of graph solutions.*

Drawing Histograms (page 27)

1. (a) Tally chart totals as below:

Weight group	Total
45-49.9	1
50-54.9	2
55-59.9	7 (given)
60-64.9	13
65-69.9	15
70-74.9	13
75-79.9	11
80-84.9	16
85-89.9	9
90-94.9	5
95-99.9	2
100-104.9	0
105-109.9	1

(b) Histogram: *See the next page of graph solutions.*

Drawing Pie Graphs (page 28)

1. (a) Tabulated data:

Food item in diet	Stoats		Rats		Cats	
	% in diet	Angle /°	% in diet	Angle /°	% in diet	Angle /°
Birds	23.6	85	1.4	5	6.9	25
Crickets	15.3	55	23.6	85	-	-
Insects	15.3	55	20.8	75	1.9	7
Voles	9.2	33	-	-	19.4	70
Rabbits	8.3	30	-	-	18.1	65
Rats	6.1	22	-	-	43.1	155
Mice	13.9	50	-	-	10.6	38
Fruits	-	-	40.3	145	-	-
Leaves	-	-	13.9	50	-	-
Unid.	8.3	30	-	-	-	-

(b) Pie graphs: *See the next page of graph solutions.*

Drawing Kite Graphs (page 29)

1. (a) Table:

Distance from mouth/ km	Wet weight/ $g\,m^{-2}$		
	Stn A	Stn B	Stn C
0	0.4	0.4	0
0.5	0.5	0.6	0.5
1.0	0.4	0.1	0
1.5	0.3	0.5	0.2
2.0	0.3	0.4	-
2.5	0.6	0.3	-
3.0	0.1	-	-
3.5	0.7	-	-
4.0	0.2	-	-
4.5	2.5	-	-
5.0	0.3	-	-

(b) Kite graph: *See the next page of graph solutions.*

Drawing Line Graphs (page 30)

1. (a) Line graph:

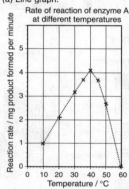

Rate of reaction of enzyme A at different temperatures

(b) Rate of reaction at 15°C = 1.6 mg product min^{-1}

2. (a) Line graph: See next page of graph solutions.

(b) The data suggest that the deer population is being controlled by the wolves. Deer numbers increase to a peak when wolf numbers are at their lowest; the deer population then declines (and continues declining) when wolf numbers increase and then peak. **Note**: A scenario of apparent control of the deer population by the wolves is suggested, but not confirmed, by the data. In natural systems, this suggestion (of prey control by a large predator) *may* be specious; most large predators do not control their prey (except perhaps at low population densities in certain systems), but are themselves controlled by the numbers of available prey, which are regulated by other factors such as food availability. In this case, the wolves were introduced for the purpose of controlling deer and were probably doing so. However, an equally valid interpretation of the data could be that the wolves are responding to changes in deer numbers (with the usual lag inherent in population responses), and the deer were already peaking in response to

Drawing bar graphs:

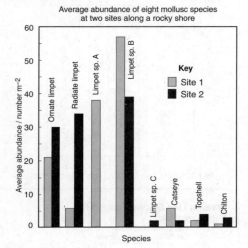

Average abundance of eight mollusc species at two sites along a rocky shore

Drawing histograms:

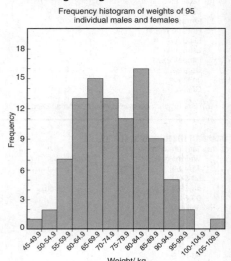

Frequency histogram of weights of 95 individual males and females

Drawing pie graphs:

Key to food items in the diet

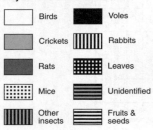

Percentage occurrence of different food items in the diets of stoats, rats, and cats

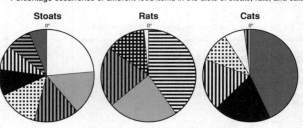

Drawing kite graphs:

Distribution of invertebrates along 3 different streams as indicated by biomass measured as wet weight/ g m⁻²

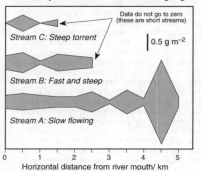

Drawing line graphs: Plotting multiple data sets

Numbers of deer and wolves on an island forest reserve between 1961 and 1969

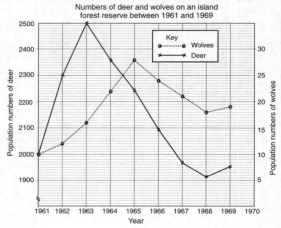

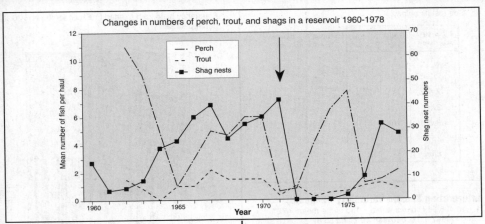

Changes in numbers of perch, trout, and shags in a reservoir 1960-1978

factors about which we have no information.

3. (a) Line graph and (b) point at which shags and nests were removed: See the graph above.

Interpreting Line & Scatter Graphs (page 33)

1. (b) **Slope**: Negative linear relationship, with constantly falling slope.
   Interpretation: Variable Y decreases steadily with increase in variable X.
   (c) **Slope**: Constant, level slope.
   Interpretation: Increase in variable X does not affect variable Y.
   (d) **Slope**: Slope rises and then becomes level.
   Interpretation: Variable Y initially increases with increase in variable X, then levels out (no further increase with increase in variable X).
   (e) **Slope**: Rises, peaks and then falls.
   Interpretation: Variable Y initially increases with increase in variable X, peaks and then declines with further increase in variable X.
   (f) **Slope**: Exponentially increasing slope.
   Interpretation: As variable X increases, variable Y increases exponentially.

2. The data suggest that the deer population is being controlled by the wolves. Deer numbers increase to a peak when wolf numbers are at their lowest; the deer population then declines (and continues declining) when wolf numbers increase and then peak.
   Note: A scenario of apparent control of the deer population by the wolves is suggested, but not confirmed, by the data. In natural systems, this may be a specious suggestion; most large predators do not usually control their prey, but are themselves controlled by the numbers of available prey, which are regulated by other factors such as food availability. In this case, the wolves were introduced for the purpose of controlling deer and were probably doing so. However, an equally valid interpretation of the data could be that the wolves are responding to changes in deer numbers (with the usual lag inherent in population responses), and the deer were already peaking in response to factors about which we have no information.

Drawing Scatter Plots (page 34)

1. (a) Scatter plot and (b) Line of best fit:

Oxygen consumption of fish with affected gills

2. (a) At rest: No clear relationship; the line on the graph appears to have no significant slope (although this could be tested). **Note**: There is a slight tendency for oxygen consumption to fall as more of the gill becomes affected, but the scatter of points precludes making any conclusions about this.
   (b) Swimming: A negative linear relationship; the greater the proportion of affected gill, the lower the oxygen consumption.

3. The gill disease appears to have little or no effect on the oxygen uptake in resting fish.

Descriptive Statistics (page 37)

1. The modal value and associated ranked entries indicate that the variable being measured (spores per frond) has a bimodal distribution i.e. the data are not normally distributed. (Therefore) the mean and median are not accurate indicators of central tendency. Note also that the median differs from the mean; also an indication of a skewed (non-normal) distribution.

2. See results below:

Beetle mass /g	Tally	Total
2.1	I	1
2.2	II	2
2.4	I\	2
2.5	////I	4
2.6	///I	3
2.7	I	1
2.8	I\	2

Median = 8th value when in rank order = 2.5

Mode = 2.5

Mean = 2.49 ~ 2.5

Interpreting Sample Variability (page 39)

1. (a) 496/689 values within ± 1sd of the mean = 72% (48±7.8, i.e. between 40.2 and 55.8)
   (b) 671//689 values within ± 2 sd of the mean = 97% (48± 15.6, i.e. between 32.4 and 63.6)
   (c) The data are very close to being normally distributed about the mean (normal distribution + 67% of values lie within 1sd of the mean and 95% of values lie between 2 sd of the mean).

2. The mean and the median are very close.

3. N = 30 data set
   (a) **Mean** = 49.23
   (b) **Median** = 49.5
   (c) **Mode** = 38
   (d) **Sample variance** =129.22
   (e) **Standard deviation** = 11.37

4. N = 50 data set
   (a) **Mean** = 61.44
   (b) **Median** = 63
   (c) **Mode** = 64
   (d) **Sample variance** = 14.59
   (e) **Standard deviation** = 3.82

5. Frequency histogram (plotted in *Excel*) for the N=50 perch data set.

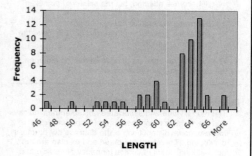

Frequency histogram (plotted in *Excel*) for the N = 30 perch data set.

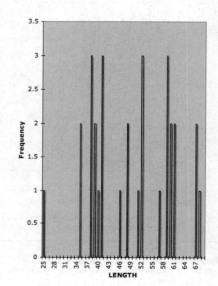

6. (a) The mean and median are very close to each other for the N=30 data set. There is a larger difference between the mean and median values obtained in the N=50 data set.
   (b) The standard deviation obtained for the N=30 set is much larger (11.37) compared to only 3.82 for the larger N=50 data set.
   (c) The N=30 data set more closely resembles the complete data set. The mean and median are quite close to those of the original data set. The mean, median and mode for the N=50 data set are considerably higher than those statistics for the complete data set. The sample variance and standard deviation values for the complete data set fall between those of the two smaller data sets.

7. (a) The frequency histogram for the N=30 data set shows a relatively normal distribution of data. The frequency histogram for the N=50 data set shows a non-normal distribution which is skewed to the right (negative skew).
   (b) The person who collected the sample in the N=30 data set used equipment and techniques designed to collect fish randomly. As a result, a normal distribution of fish sizes was obtained by their sampling methods. Fish collection for the N=50 sample set was biased. The mesh size used did not retain smaller fish, so a larger proportion of bigger fish were collected. When plotted on a frequency histogram the data presented as a negative skew.

Biological Drawings (page 41)

1. (a)-(h) any eight features in any order:
   – Lines cross over each other and are angled.
   – Cells are inaccurately drawn: they are not closed

shapes, they do not even nearly represent what is actually there, there are overlaps.
- There is no magnification given.
- Drawing is cramped at the top corner of the page.
- Labels are drawn on an angle.
- There is no indication of whether the section is a cross section or longitudinal section.
- There is a line to a cell type that has no label
- Shading is inappropriate and does not indicate anything. It is apparently random and is unnecessary.
- The material being drawn has not been identified accurately in the title by species.

2. Student's response required here. Some desirable features are shown in the figure on the top of the next column, but page position and size cannot be shown.

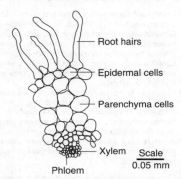

Root tranverse section from <u>Ranunculus</u>

3. A **biological drawing** is designed to convey useful information about the structure of an organism. From such diagrams another person should be able to clearly identify similar organisms and structures. By contrast, **artistic drawings** exhibit 'artistic licence' where the image is a single person's impression of what they saw. It may not be a reliable source of visual information about the structure of the organism.

The Structure of a Report (page 43)
1. (b) **Methods**: provides the reader with instructions on how the investigation was carried out and what equipment was used. Allows for the procedures to be repeated and confirmed by other investigators.
   (c) **Results:** Provides the findings of the investigation and allows the reader to evaluate these themselves.
   (d) **Discussion:** The findings of the work are discussed in detail so the reader can evaluate the findings. Design limitations, and ways the work could have been improved are also presented.
   (e) **References/Acknowledgments:** Lists sources of information and help used during the investigation. The reader can review the references for more detail if required, and compare your work with other studies in the area of investigation.

2. A poster presents all of the key information from an investigation in an attractive, concise manner which is readily accessible and easy to read. People can quickly determine if the study is of interest to them, and the

references provide an opportunity to find out further information if required.

Writing the Methods (page 44)
1. (a)-(h) Any of the following in any order:
   - Number of worms used not stated.
   - No description of the pond (size, water depth etc.).
   - Actual "room" temperature not stated.
   - Date somewhat irrelevant (time of year could be).
   - Source of sea water not stated.
   - Pre-experimental conditions of the worms not stated.
   - Volume of 100% sea water used not stated.
   - Dilution of sea water not stated.
   - Volume of diluted sea water used not stated.
   - Weighing equipment used not stated.
   - Time interval for reweighing not stated.

Writing Your Results (page 45)
1. Referring to tables and figures in the text clearly indicates which data you are referring to in your synopsis of the results and gives the reader access to these data so that they can assess your interpretation.

2. Tables summarise data and provide a record of the data values, which may not be easily obtained from a graph. Figures (graphs) present information in a way that makes trends or relationships in the data apparent. Such trends may not be evident from the tabulated data. Both formats are valuable for different reasons.

Writing Your Discussion (page 46)
1. Discussion of weaknesses in your study shows that you have considered these and acknowledged them and the effect that they may have had on the outcome of your investigation. It also provides the opportunity for those repeating the investigation (including yourself) to improve on aspects of the design.

2. A **critical evaluation** shows that you have examined your results carefully in light of the question(s) you asked and the predictions you made. Objective evaluation enables you to provide reasonable explanations for any unexpected or conflicting results and identify ways in which to improve your study design in future investigations.

3. The conclusion allows you to make a clear statement about your findings, i.e. whether for not the results support your hypothesis. If your results and discussion have been convincing, the reader should be in agreement with the conclusion you make.

Citing and Listing References (page 47)
1. A bibliography lists all sources of information whereas a reference list includes only those sources that are cited in the text. Usually a bibliography is used to compile the final reference list, which appears in the report.

2. Internet articles can be updated as new information becomes available and the original account is revised. It is important that this is noted because people using that source in the future may find information that was unavailable to the author making the original citation.

3. Reference list as follows:
Ball, P. (1996): Living factories. New Scientist, 2015, 28-31
Campbell, N. (1993): Biology. Benjamin/Cummings. Ca.
Cooper, G. (1997): The cell: a molecular approach.
ASM Press, Washington DC. pp. 75-85
Moore, P. (1996): Fuelled for Life. New Scientist, 2012, 1-4
O'Hare, L. & O'Hare, K. (1996): Food biotechnology. Biological Sciences Review, 8(3), 25.
Roberts, I. & Taylor, S. (1996): Development of a procedure for purification of a recombinant therapeutic protein. Australasian Biotechnology, 6(2), 93-99.

Report Checklist (page 49)
To be competed by the student.

The Causes of Disease (page 51)
1. An organism has a number of regions where its tissues interface with the environment; the skin, the respiratory system, the gut, and the urinogenital tract. These regions represent places where the body's tissues are in contact with the environment and where pathogens can invade the host more easily and gain entry to vulnerable tissues. For example, pathogenic microbes (cold virus, *Influenzavirus*, *M. tuberculosis*) can enter respiratory passages and penetrate gas exchange surfaces, *Vibrio cholerae* bacterium can be ingested with contaminated food or water and penetrate the defences of the gut epithelium, causing a change in ion transort and diarrhoea, vectors for pathogens (such as mosquitoes) can penetrate the skin's surface providing a way in which a pathogen (e.g. *Plasmodium*) can enter host tissues.

2. Multiple risk factors can work together to markedly increase the risk of developing a disease. In the case of cardiovascular disease, having any one of three risk factors (high blood lipids, glucose intolerance, or hypertension) increases risk of CVD by 1.5 to 2.3 times the level of risk of someone without those risk factors. When two of these risk factors are present, the risk level increases to 2.8-4X. When all three risk factors are present, the risk of developing the disease increases to over 6X. Multiple risk factors are commonly associated because the same dietary/lifestyle factors often contribute to different risk factors (e.g. hypertension, high blood lipids, and glucose intolerance are all associated with another risk factor - obesity). Smoking increases risk in these patients too because of its effects on the cardiovascular system.

Biochemical Tests (page 54)
1. $R_f = 15$ mm $\div 33$ mm $= \mathbf{0.45}$

2. R_f must always be less than one because the substance cannot move further than the solvent front.

3. Chromatography would be an appropriate technique if the sample was very small or when the substance of interest contains a mixture of several different compounds and neither is predominant.

4. Immersion would just wash out the substance into solution instead of separating the components out behind a solvent front.

5. Leucine, arginine, alanine, glycine (most soluble to least soluble).

6. Lipids are insoluble in water. They will not form an emulsion in water unless they have first been dissolved in ethanol (a non-polar solvent).

Carbohydrates (page 55)
1. Polysaccharides are complex carbohydrates made up of many monosaccharides joined together. They are excellent sources of energy because they can be easily converted into monosaccharide sugars (e.g. glucose) by hydrolysis when energy is needed. Monosaccharide sugars are the primary source of cellular fuel.

2. (a) Compound sugars are formed and broken down by condensation and hydrolysis reactions respectively. **Condensation reactions** join two carbohydrate molecules by a glycosidic bond with the release of a water molecule. **Hydrolysis reactions** use water to split a carbohydrate molecule into two, where the water molecule is used to provide a hydrogen atom and a hydroxyl group.
   (b) In general terms, enzymes break the glycosidic bonds between disaccharides resulting in the production of smaller carbohydrate chains or monosaccharides. The enzyme **maltase** breaks down (hydrolyses) the disaccharide maltose into two molecules of α-glucose. The processes utilises a water molecule for the sources of the hydrogen and hydroxyl group.

3. (a) Lactase catalyses the hydrolysis of the disaccharide lactose into its constituent galactose and glucose monomers.
   (b) Disaccharides cannot be absorbed through the gut wall, so in the absence of lactase, the lactose in ingested dairy products remains uncleaved and passes intact into the colon. In the presence of lactose, bacteria in the gut switch over to lactose metabolism (a preferred but rare substrate), and the resultant fermentation produces copious amounts of gas (a mixture of hydrogen, carbon dioxide, and methane). This, in turn, causes the bloating and flatulence associated with the intolerance.

4. Starch and glycogen are both glucose polymers, but differ in form and function because of the length of the polymers and the degree of branching. **Starch** is a mixture of two polysaccharides: amylose (unbranched with α-1,4 glycosidic bonds) and amylopectin (branched with α-1,6 glycosidic bonds). The α-1,4 glycosidic bonds and combination of branched and unbranched chains account for starch being less soluble and less easily hydrolysed than glycogen. **Glycogen** is similar to amylopectin, being composed of α-glucose molecules, but it is larger and there are more α-1,6 links. This makes it highly branched, more soluble, and more easily hydrolysed than starch. The differences in solubility make relatively insoluble starch the carbohydrate storage compound of choice in plant tissues whereas, in animals, carbohydrate is stored in the more soluble form of glycogen.

Amino Acids (page 57)

1. Amino acids are the building blocks for constructing proteins (which have diverse structural and metabolic functions). Amino acids are also the precursors of many important molecules (e.g. neurotransmitters and hormones).

2. The side chains (R groups) differ in their chemical structure (and therefore their chemical effect).

3. Translation of the genetic code. Genetic instructions from the chromosomes (genes on the DNA) determine the order in which amino acids are joined together.

4. **Essential amino acids** cannot be manufactured by the human body, they must be included in the food we eat.

5. **Condensation reactions** involve the joining of two amino acids (or an amino acid to a dipeptide or polypeptide) by a peptide bond with the release of a water molecule.

6. **Hydrolysis** involves the splitting of a dipeptide (or the splitting of an amino acid from a polypeptide) where the peptide bond is broken and a water molecule is used to provide a hydrogen atom and a hydroxyl group.

7. The L-form.

Proteins (page 59)

1. (a) **Structural**: Proteins form an important component of connective tissues and epidermal structures: collagen, keratin (hair, horn etc.). Proteins are also found scattered on, in, and through cell membranes, but tend to have a regulatory role in this instance. Proteins are also important in maintaining a tightly coiled structure in a condensed chromosome.
   (b) **Regulatory**: Hormones such as insulin, adrenaline (modified amino acid), glucagon (peptide) are chemical messengers released from glands to trigger a response in a target tissue. They help maintain homeostasis. **Enzymes** regulate metabolic processes in cells.
   (c) **Contractile**: Actin and myosin are structural components of muscle fibres. Using a ratchet system, these two proteins move past each other when energy is supplied.
   (d) **Immunological**: Gamma globulins are blood proteins that act as antibodies, targeting antigens (foreign substances and microbes) for immobilisation and destruction.
   (e) **Transport**: Haemoglobin and myoglobin are proteins that act as carrier molecules for transporting oxygen in the bloodstream of vertebrates. Invertebrates usually have some other type of oxygen carrying molecule in the blood.
   (f) **Catalytic**: Enzymes, e.g. amylase, lipase, lactase, trypsin, are involved in the chemical digestion of food. A vast variety of other enzymes are involved in just about every metabolic process in organisms.

2. Denaturation destroys protein function because it involves an irreversible change in the precise tertiary or quaternary structure that confers biological activity. For example, a denatured enzyme protein may not have its reactive sites properly aligned, and will be prevented from attracting the substrate molecule.

3. Any one of:
   - Globular proteins have a tertiary structure that

produces a globular or spherical shape. Fibrous proteins have a tertiary structure that produces long chains or sheets, often with many cross-linkages.
   - The structure of fibrous proteins makes them insoluble in water. The spherical nature of globular proteins makes them water soluble.

4. (a) 21 amino acids   (b) 29 amino acids

Enzymes (page 61)

1. Catalysts cause reactions to occur more readily. Enzymes are biological molecules (usually proteins) and allow reactions that would not otherwise take place to proceed, or they speed up a reaction that takes place only slowly. Hence the term, **biological catalyst**. The **active site** is critical to this function, as it is the region where substrate molecules are drawn in and positioned in such a way as to promote the reaction.

2. **Catabolism** involves metabolic reactions that break large molecules into smaller ones. Such reactions include digestion and cellular respiration. They release energy and are therefore **exergonic**. In contrast, **anabolism** involves metabolic reactions that build larger molecules from smaller ones. Anabolic reactions include protein synthesis and photosynthesis. They require the input of energy and are **endergonic**.

3. The **lock and key model** proposed that the substrate was simply drawn into a closely matching cleft (active site) on the enzyme. In this model, the enzyme's active site was a somewhat passive recipient of the substrate.

4. The **induced fit model** is a modified version of lock and key, where the substrate fits into the active site, and this initiates a change in the shape of the enzyme's active site so that the reaction can proceed.

5. (a) and (b) in any order, any two of:
   - Deviations from the optimum pH.
   - Excessively high temperature (heating).
   - Treatment with heavy metal ions, urea, organic solvents, or detergents.

   All these agents denature proteins by disrupting the non-covalent bonds maintaining the protein's functional secondary and tertiary structure. The covalent bonds providing the primary structure often remain intact but the protein loses solubility and the functional shape of the protein (its active site) is lost.

6. A mutation could result in a different amino acid being positioned in the polypeptide chain. The final protein may be folded incorrectly (incorrect tertiary and quaternary structure) and lose its biological function. **Note**: If the mutation is silent or in a non-critical region of the enzyme, biological function may not be affected.

Enzyme Reaction Rates (page 63)

1. (a) An increase in enzyme concentration increases reaction rate.
   (b) By manufacturing more or less (increasing or decreasing the rate of protein synthesis).

2. (a) An increase in **substrate concentration** increases reaction rate to a point. Reaction rate does not continue increasing but levels off as the amount of substrate continues to increase.

(b) The reaction rate changes because after a certain substrate level the enzymes are fully saturated by substrate and the rate cannot increase any more.

3. (a) An optimum **temperature** for an enzyme is the temperature at which enzyme activity is maximum.
   (b) Most enzymes perform poorly at low temperatures because chemical reactions occur slowly or not all at low temperatures (enzyme activity will reappear when the temperature increases; usually enzymes are not damaged by moderately low temperatures).

4. (a) Optimum **pH**: Pepsin: 1-2, trypsin: approx. 7.5-8.2, urease: approx. 6.5-7.0
   (b) The stomach is an acidic environment which is the ideal pH for pepsin.

Enzyme Cofactors and Inhibitors (page 64)

1. **Cofactors** are non-protein molecules or ions that are required for proper functioning of an enzyme either by altering the shape of the enzyme to complete the active site or by making the active site more reactive (improving the substrate-enzyme fit).

2. (a) Arsenic, lead, mercury, cadmium.
   (b) Heavy metals are toxic because they bind to the active sites of enzymes and permanently inactivate them. While the active site is occupied by the heavy metal the enzyme is non-functional. Because they are lost exceedingly slowly from the body, anything other than a low level of these metals is toxic.

3. (a) Examples: nerve gases, cyanide, DDT, parathion, pyrethrins (insecticides).
   (b) **Nerve gases** poison acetylcholinesterase, which is an important enzyme in the functioning of nerves and muscles (it normally deactivates acetylcholine in synapses and prevents continued over-response of nerve and muscle cells).
   Cyanide poisons the enzyme cytochrome oxidase, one of the enzymes in the electron transport system. It therefore stops cellular respiration.
   DDT and other organochlorines: Inhibitors of key enzymes in the nervous system.
   Pyrethrins: Insecticides which inactivate enzymes at the synapses of invertebrates. This has a similar over-excitation effect as nerve gases in mammals.

4. In **competitive inhibition**, the inhibitor competes with the substrate for the enzyme's active site and, once in place, prevents substrate binding. A **noncompetitive inhibitor** does not occupy the active site but binds to some other part of the enzyme, making it less able to perform its function as an effective biological catalyst.

5. Whilst noncompetitive inhibitors reduce the activity of the enzyme and slow down the reaction rate, **allosteric inhibitors** block the active site altogether and prevent its functioning completely.

The Human Digestive Tract (page 65)

1. Structure as follows:
   A: Mouth and teeth
   B: Salivary glands
   C: Oesophagus
   D: Liver
   E: Stomach
   F: Pancreas
   G: Gall bladder
   H: Colon (large intestine)
   I: Small intestine
   J: Rectum
   K: Appendix
   L: Anus

   Region responsible for each stated function as follows:
   a: I - small intestine
   b: J - rectum
   c: H - colon
   d: E - stomach
   e: F - pancreas (or B)
   f: D - liver
   g: B - salivary glands

2. Anal sphincter (AS) at the end of the anus.
   Pyloric sphincter (PS) between the stomach and small intestine.
   Cardiac sphincter (CS) between the oesophagus and stomach.

3. a: Tongue
   b: Villi lining the small intestine (ileum)
   c: Villi lining the lumen of the small intestine (duodenum)
   d: Lining (mucosa) of the stomach
   e: Teeth
   f: Liver

4. The bolus (rounded mass of chewed food) moves through the gut by peristalsis. Circular muscles contract behind the bolus, pushing it down. Ahead of the bolus, the longitudinal muscles contract shortening the passage and making it wider to reach the food.

5. It allows the gut to become regionally specialised so that different parts of the gut perform different functions. e.g. storage, physical digestion, chemical digestion, elimination, water reabsorption. This improves the overall efficiency of the digestive process.

6. Diet (degree of bulk and nutritional quality). Note: bulky, low energy diets required larger, longer guts that can accommodate large volumes of food.

7. (a) Mastication provides physical break down of food by chewing. The result is greater surface area for the action of enzymes.
   (b) Absorption provides the means by which the products of chemical digestion enter the bloodstream. Absorption of water and salts in the large intestine is important in fluid and ion balance and prevents excess water loss from the gut.

Stomach and Small Intestine (page 67)

1. The gut movements move food through the gut by peristalsis and mix the food so it is accessible to digestive enzymes.

2. The stomach is a sac-like organ, lined with folds, which enable considerable expansion of the walls. This allows the stomach to accommodate large volumes of food and serves as a storage organ between meals. The stomach lining is pitted with gastric glands, which

secrete mucus, and a precursor of the protein-digesting enzyme, pepsin. The acid activates the precursor and the pepsin begins the process of protein digestion. The mucus protects the stomach lining from the acid and lubricates the food as it is mixed by the muscular stomach walls. Mixing also helps to expose the food in the stomach to the action of the pepsin.

3. (a) and (b): any two of the following in any order:
Site: Stomach
Enzyme: Pepsin
Purpose: Digestion of proteins to polypeptides.

Site: Pancreas
Enzyme: Pancreatic amylase
Purpose: Digestion of starch to maltose

Site: Pancreas
Enzyme: Trypsin/chymotrypsin
Purpose: Digestion of proteins to polypeptides.

Site: Pancreas
Enzyme: Pancreatic lipase
Purpose: Digestion of fats to fatty acids and glycerol.

Site: Pancreas
Enzyme: Peptidases
Purpose: Digestion of polypeptides of amino acids.

Site: Intestinal mucosa
Enzyme: Peptidases
Purpose: Digestion of polypeptides to amino acids.

Site: Intestinal mucosa
Enzyme: Maltase, lactase, sucrase.
Purpose: Digestion of carbohydrates (maltose, lactose, sucrose respectively) into their constituent parts.

4. (a) The enzymes involved in digestion in different regions of the gut have specific pH optima (pH at which they operate most efficiently). Note: For pepsin (stomach) this optimum is acid pH 1.5-2.0, for enzymes in the small intestine, the optimum is alkaline pH 7.5-8.2.
   (b) The enzymes are secreted as inactive precursors in order to prevent their activity in the site of production and release (where they would damage the tissue). Once in the gut lumen, they an be activated to digest the food (the gut lining itself is protected by mucus).

5. Alcohol is a small molecule and is absorbed directly from the stomach into the bloodstream. When the stomach is empty, the mucosa is more exposed than when then stomach is full of food and the absorption can take place much more rapidly.

6. Sphincters regulate the passage of food through the gut, allowing material to pass more quickly through the gut, or holding it back. Their activity depends on speed of digestion, food type, the influence of hormones, and the fullness of the gut. Note: Sphincter contraction partly or completely closes and orifice.

The Large Intestine (page 69)

1. Reabsorption of water from the slurry of digested food.

2. Less dependent on a large surface area (required in the small intestine for efficient nutrient absorption). Mucus secretion from short, tubular glands is more important (for protection of the epithelium from friction).

3. (a) Lymph nodule
   (b) Submucosa
   (c) Epithelium
   (d) Circular muscle

Absorption and Transport (page 70)

1. (a) Micelles: Aid the passage of lipids across the membrane of epithelial cells.
   (b) Chylomicrons: These aggregations of fats are coated with protein in such a way that the fat remains in suspension during transport.

2. It is important that nutrient-rich blood from the gut is taken directly to the liver so that the nutrients can be removed and processed most efficiently. Note: Nutrient-rich blood has a high osmotic potential and therefore also represents a potential threat to homeostasis. Rapid removal of the nutrients from the blood is therefore desirable in terms of maintaining homeostasis.

The Control of Digestion (page 71)

1. (a) Food in the mouth causes a reflex stimulation of salivary glands and stomach (parasympathetic stimulation via the vagus). The effect is a marked increase in salivary and gastric secretion.
   (b) Presence of fat and acid in the small intestine stimulates release of cholecystokinin and secretin from the intestinal mucosa. These hormones inhibit gastric motility and stimulate the secretions of the pancreas, the production and release of bile, and the secretions of the intestinal glands.
   (c) Stretching of the stomach stimulates the reflex secretion of the hormone gastrin from the gastric mucosa. Gastrin acts back on the stomach to increase gastric secretion and motility.

2. The vagus nerve provides the parasympathetic innervation of the gut, stimulating salivary, gastric, and pancreatic secretion.

Animal Cells (page 73)

1. The many tiny infoldings of the intestinal microvilli provide a very large surface area over which nutrients can be absorbed. This speeds up the processing of food, which is an essential feature of providing for high energy demands.

2. (a) Intestinal epithelium: The mucus secreting cells here are the **goblet cells**. They secrete mucus to protect the epithelium from abrasion and from the action of the enzymes involved in digesting the food.
   (b) Stomach: The mucus secreting cells here are the **mucous cells**. Their secretions protect the stomach epithelium from the highly acidic, protein digesting environment.

3. The stomach lining is pitted with gastric glands, which

contain the specialised cells (mucous cells, parietal cells, and chief cells) to secrete mucus, acid, and an enzyme precursor, pepsinogen. Although the stomach has folds, or rugae, to accommodate expansion of volume, its surface is not so greatly infolded as that of the small intestine, where the epithelium is pushed up into villi, and each villus has many fingerlike protrusions (microvilli) that project into the intestinal lumen. The intestinal glands lie between the villi, and secrete mucus (from goblet cells) and an alkaline fluid. The enzymes secreted by the intestinal epithelium are bound to the surfaces of the epithelial cells.

4. A: Neurone: Specialised for the generation and maintenance of electrical impulses. Long extensions of the cell body carry electrical impulses towards connections with other cells.

    B: White blood cell: Large cells, some are mobile and capable of phagocytosis, others produce substances such as histamine or antibodies, which are involved in the body's defence responses.

    C: Red blood cell: Small cells, lacking nuclei and packed with haemoglobin, which binds oxygen and transports it around the body. Relatively short lived cells with a rapid turnover.

Eukaryotic Cell Diversity (page 75)

1. (a) **Plant cells**: Mesophyll cell, vessel element (note that this is a dead cell), guard cells.
    (b) **Characteristics**: Cellulose cell wall, chloroplasts containing the photosynthetic pigments chlorophyll *a* and *b*, carbohydrate stored as starch, large vacuoles.

2. (a) **Animal cells**: Osteocyte, leucocyte, smooth muscle cell, epidermal cells of skin, neurone, erythrocyte.
    (b) **Characteristics**: No cellulose cell wall, no chloroplasts or plastids of any kind, vacuoles if present are small, no regular geometric shape.

3. (a) **Protoctistans**: *Amoeba, Euglena, Paramecium, Spirogyra, Chlamydomonas*.
    (b) **Characteristics**: A very diverse group (the eukaryotes that do not fit into plant, animal, or fungi classification). Generally refers to unicellular eukaryotes, although some primitive multicellular organisms have been included in recent years. Includes protozoans which are heterotrophic (animal-like in their nutrition), and algae, which have chloroplasts and are autotrophic (plant-like in their nutrition). A difficult group to give general characteristics for because they are so diverse. Often ciliated (e.g. *Paramecium*) or flagellated (e.g. *Euglena*). Note that the cyanobacteria are now classified within Prokaryotae (not Protoctista).

4. (a) **Fungal cells**: Yeast, pin mould hyphae.
    (b) **Characteristics**: Eukaryotes, usually multicellular, all are heterotrophs (no photosynthetic ability), lack chloroplasts. Except in yeasts, the basic fungus body is composed of basic building blocks called hyphae. Cell walls composed mainly of chitin.

Cell Sizes (page 76)

1. (a) *Amoeba*:   300 µm   0.3 mm
    (b) Foraminiferan: 400 µm   0.4 mm
    (c) *Leptospira*:   7-8 µm   0.007-0.008 mm
    (d) Epidermis: 120 µm   0.12 mm
    (e) *Daphnia*:   2500 µm   2.5 mm
    (f) *Papillomavirus*: 0.13 µm   0.00013 mm

2. *Papillomavirus*; *Leptospira*; Epidermis (but not an organism); *Amoeba*; Foraminiferan; *Daphnia*

3. Onion epidermis (possibly); *Amoeba*; foraminiferan; *Daphnia*

4. (a) 0.00025 mm   (b) 0.45 mm   (c) 0.0002 mm

Cell Structures and Organelles (page 77)

(b) **Name**: Ribosome
   Location: Free in cytoplasm or bound to rough ER
   Function: Synthesize polypeptides (=proteins)
   Present in plant cells: Yes
   Present in animal cells: Yes
   Visible under LM: No

(c) **Name**: Mitochondrion
   Location: In cytoplasm as discrete organelles
   Function: Site of cellular respiration (ATP formation)
   Present in plant cells: Yes
   Present in animal cells: Yes
   Visible under LM: Not with most standard school LM, but can be seen using high quality, high power LM.

(d) **Name**: Golgi apparatus
   Location: In cytoplasm associated with the smooth endoplasmic reticulum, often close to the nucleus.
   Function: Final modification of proteins and lipids. Sorting and storage for use in the cell or packaging molecules for export.
   Present in plant cells: Yes
   Present in animal cells: Yes
   Visible under LM: Not with most standard school LM, but may be visible using high quality, high power LM.

(e) **Name**: Endoplasmic reticulum (in this case, rough ER)
   Location: Penetrates the whole cytoplasm
   Function: Involved in the transport of materials (e.g. proteins) within the cell and between the cell and its surroundings.
   Present in plant cells: Yes
   Present in animal cells: Yes
   Visible under LM: No

(f) **Name**: Cytoskeleton
   Location: Throughout cytoplasm
   Function: Provides structure and shape to a cell, responsible for cell movement (e.g. during muscle contraction), and provides intracellular transport of organelles and other structures.
   Present in plant cells: Yes
   Present in animal cells: Yes
   Visible under LM: No

(g) **Name**: Lysosome and food vaculoe (given)
   Lysosome
   Location: Free in cytoplasm.
   Function: Ingests and destroys foreign material. Able to digest the cell itself under some circumstances.
   Present in plant cells: Yes but variably (vacuoles may have a lysosomal function in some plant cells).
   Present in animal cells: Yes
   Visible under LM: No

Vacuole (a food vacuole in an animal cell is shown, so students may answer with respect to this).
Location: In cytoplasm.
Function: In plant cells, the vacuole (often only one) is a large fluid filled structure involved in storage and support (turgor). In animal cells, vacuoles are smaller and more numerous, and are involved in storage (of water, wastes, and soluble pigments).
Present in plant cells: Yes, as (a) large structure(s).
Present in animal cells: Yes, smaller, more numerous
Visible under LM: Yes in plant cells, no in animal cells.

(h) **Name**: Nucleus
Location: Discrete organelle, position is variable.
Function: The control center of the cell; the site of the nuclear material (DNA).
Present in plant cells: Yes
Present in animal cells: Yes
Visible under LM: Yes.

(i) **Name**: Centrioles
Location: In cytoplasm, usually next to the nucleus.
Function: Involved in cell division (probably in the organisation of the spindle fibers).
Present in plant cells: Variably (absent in higher plants)
Present in animal cells: Yes
Visible under LM: No.

(j) **Name**: Cilia and flagella (given)
Location: Anchored in the cell membrane and extending outside the cell.
Function: Motility.
Present in plant cells: No
Present in animal cells: Yes
Visible under LM: Variably (depends on magnification and preparation/fixation of material).

Prokaryotic Cells (page 79)

1. (a) The nuclear material (DNA) is not contained within a clearly defined nucleus with a nuclear membrane.
   (b) Membrane-bound cellular organelles (e.g. mitochondria, endoplasmic reticulum) are missing.
   (c) Single, circular chromosome sometimes with accessory chromosomes called plasmids.

2. (a) Locomotion: Flagella enable bacterial movement out of unsuitable conditions to preferred conditions.
   (b) Fimbriae are shorter, straighter, and thinner than flagella. Used for attachment rather than locomotion.

3. (a) Bacterial cell wall lies outside the plasma (cell surface) membrane. It is a semi-rigid structure composed of a macromolecule called peptidoglycan, and contains varying amounts of lipopolysacchardies and lipoproteins.
   (b) The glycocalyx is a viscous, gelatinous layer which lies outside the cell wall. It usually comprises polysaccharide and/or polypeptide, but not peptidoglycan, and may be firmly or loosely attached to the wall.

4. (a) Bacteria usually reproduce by binary fission, where the DNA replicates and the cell then splits into two.
   (b) Conjugation differs from binary fission in that DNA is exchanged between one bacterial cell (the donor) and another (the recipient). The recipient cell gains DNA from the donor.

5. A number of features contribute to the ability of bacteria to causes disease, although not all bacteria possess all features. These include:

– Rapid rates of growth and division in the right environment, which speeds up invasion of the host's tissues and means that evolutionary changes affecting virulence occur rapidly)
– An ability to acquire genes affecting virulence through conjugation (horizontal evolution). – Ability to form resistant endospores which remain viable to reinfect a host at a later stage.
– Glycocalyx (capsules and slime layers) enables attachment to host tissues, contributes to virulence, and can protect from host immune defences.

Optical Microscopes (page 81)

1. (a) Eyepiece lens   (h) In-built light source
   (b) Arm   (i) Eyepiece lens
   (c) Coarse focus knob   (j) Eyepiece focus
   (d) Fine focus knob   (k) Focus knob
   (e) Objective lens   (l) Objective lens
   (f) Mechanical stage   (m) Stage
   (g) Condenser

2. Phase contrast: Used where the specimen is transparent (to increase contrast between transparent structures). **Note**: It is superior to dark field because a better image of the interior of specimens is obtained.

3. (a) Plant cell, any two of: Cell wall, nucleus (may see chromatin if stained appropriately), vacuole, cell membrane (high magnification), Golgi apparatus, mitochondria (high magnification), chloroplast, cytoplasm (if stained), nuclear envelope (maybe).
   (b) Animal cell, any two of: Nucleus (may see chromatin if stained appropriately), centriole, cell membrane (high magnification), Golgi apparatus, mitochondria (high magnification), cytoplasm (if stained).

4. Any of: Ribosomes, microtubules, endoplasmic reticulum, Golgi vesicles (free), nuclear envelope as two layers, lysosomes (animal cells). Also detail of organelles such as mitochondria and chloroplasts.

5. (a) Leishman's stain
   (b) Schultz's solution/iodine solution
   (c) Schultz's solution
   (d) Aniline sulfate/ Schultz's solution
   (e) Methylene blue
   (f) Schultz's solution

6. (a) 600X magnification   (b) 600X magnification

7. Bright field, compound light microscopes produce a flat (2-dimensional) image from a thin, transparent sample. Dissecting microscopes produce a 3-dimensional image, revealing the surface details of the specimen.

8. Magnification is the number of times larger an image is than the specimen. Resolution is the degree of achievable detail. The limit of resolution is the minimum distance by which two points in a specimen can be separated and still be distinguished as separate points. **Note**: By adding stronger, or more, lenses, a LM can magnify an image many 1000s of times but its resolution is limited. EMs have greater resolving power because of the very short wavelength of the electrons.

Electron Microscopes (page 83)

1. The limit of resolution (see #8 above) is related to wavelength (about 0.45X the wavelength). The shortest visible light has a wavelength of about 450 nm giving a resolution of 0.45 x 450 nm; close to 200 nm. Points less than 200 nm apart will be perceived as one point or a blur. Electron beams have a shorter wavelength than light so the resolution is much greater (points 0.5 nm apart can be distinguished as separate points; a resolving power that is 400X that of a light microscope).

2. (a) **TEM**: Used to (any of): show cell ultrastructure i.e. organelles; to investigate changes in the number, size, shape, or condition of cells and organelles i.e. demonstrate cellular processes or activities; to detect the presence of viruses in cells.
   (b) **SEM**: Used to (any of): show the surface features of cells, e.g. guard cell surrounding a stoma; to show the surface features of organisms for identification (often used for invertebrates and viruses); for general identification by surface feature, e.g. for pollen used in palaeoclimate or forensic research.
   (c) **Bright field**: Used for (any of): examining prepared sections of tissue for cellular detail; for examining living tissue for large scale movements, e.g. blood flow in capillaries or cytoplasmic streaming.
   (d) **Dissecting**: Used for (any of): examining living specimens for surface detail and structures; sorting material from samples (e.g. leaf litter or stream invertebrates; dissecting a small organism where greater resolution than the naked eye is required.

3. A TEM   E SEM
   B Bright field LM   F Bright field LM
   C TEM   G Dissecting LM
   D Bright field LM   H SEM

Cell Fractionation (page 85)

1. Cell organelles have different densities and spin down at different rates. Smaller organelles take longer to spin down and require a higher centrifugation speed to separate out.

2. The sample is homogenized (broken up) before centrifugation to rupture the cell surface membrane, break open the cell, and release the cell contents.

3. (a) Isotonic solution is needed so that there are no volume changes in the organelles.
   (b) Cool solution prevent self digestion of the organelles by enzymes released during homogenization.
   (c) Buffered solution prevents pH changes that might denature enzymes and other proteins.

4. (a) Ribosomes and endoplasmic reticulum
   (b) Lysosomes and mitochondria
   (c) Nuclei

Identifying Cell Structures (page 86)

1. (a) Cytoplasm   (f) Cell wall
   (b) Vacuole   (g) Chromosome
   (c) Starch granule   (h) Nuclear membrane
   (d) Chloroplast   (i) Endoplasmic reticulum
   (e) Mitochondrion   (j) Plasma membrane

2. 9 cells (1 complete cell, plus the edges of 8 others)

3. Plant cell; it has chloroplasts and a cell wall. It also has a highly geometric cell shape.

4. (a) The cytoplasm is located between the plasma membrane and the nuclear membrane (outside the nucleus).
   (b) The cytoplasm comprises a 'watery soup' of dissolved substances. In eukaryotic cells, organelles are found in the cytoplasm. Cytoplasm = cytosol (including cytoskeleton) + organelles.

5. (a) Starch granules, which occur within specialised plastids called leucoplasts. Starch granules are non-living inclusions, deposited as a reserve energy store.
   (b) Vacuoles, which are fluid filled cavities bounded by a single membrane. Plant vacuoles contain cell sap; an aqueous solution of dissolved food material, ions, waste products, and pigments. **Note**: Young plant cells (such as the one pictured) usually have several small vacuoles, which unite in a mature cell to form a large, permanent central vacuole.

Interpreting Electron Micrographs (page 87)

1. (a) Chloroplast
   (b) Plant cells, particularly in leaf and green stems.
   (c) Function: Site of photosynthesis. Captures solar energy to build glucose from CO_2 and water.
   (d)

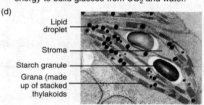

Lipid droplet

Stroma

Starch granule

Grana (made up of stacked thylakoids

2. (a) Golgi apparatus
   (b) Plant and animal cells
   (c) Function: Packages substances to be secreted by the cell. Forms a membrane vesicle containing the chemicals for export from the cell (e.g. nerve cells export neurotransmitters; endocrine glands export hormones; digestive gland cells export enzymes).

3. (a) Mitochondrion
   (b) Plant and animal cells (most common in cells that have high energy demands, such as muscle).
   (c) Function: Site of most of the process of cellular respiration, which releases energy from food (glucose) to fuel metabolism.
   (d)

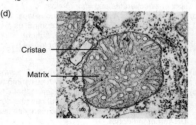

Cristae

Matrix

4. (a) Endoplasmic reticulum
   (b) Plant and animal cells (eukaryotes)
   (c) Function: Site of protein synthesis (translation

stage). Transport network that moves substances through its system of tubes. Many complex reactions need to take place on membrane surfaces.
   (d) Ribosomes.

5. (a) Nucleus
   (b) Plant and animal cells (eukaryotes)
   (c) Function: Controls cell metabolism (all the life-giving chemical reactions), and functioning of the whole organism. These instructions are inherited from one generation to the next.

   (d)

   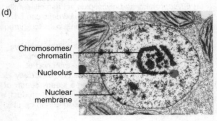

   Chromosomes/chromatin
   Nucleolus
   Nuclear membrane

6. (a) Function: Controls the entry and exit of substances into and out of the cell. Maintains a constant internal environment.

   (b)

   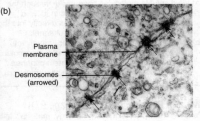

   Plasma membrane
   Desmosomes (arrowed)

7. Generalised cell.

   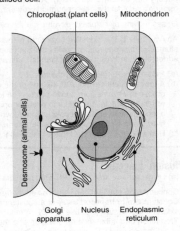

   Chloroplast (plant cells)   Mitochondrion
   Desmosome (animal cells)
   Golgi apparatus   Nucleus   Endoplasmic reticulum

Cell Processes (page 90)
1. (a) Golgi apparatus
   (b) Cytoplasm, mitochondria
   (c) Plasma membrane, vacuoles
   (d) Plasma membrane, vacuoles
   (e) Endoplasmic reticulum, ribosomes, nucleus
   (f) Chloroplasts
   (g) Centrioles, nucleus
   (h) Lysosomes
   (i) Plasma membrane, Golgi apparatus

2. **Metabolism** describes all the chemical processes of life taking place inside the cell. Examples include cellular respiration, fatty acid oxidation, photosynthesis, digestion, urea cycle, and protein synthesis.

Lipids (page 91)
1. In **phospholipids**, one of the fatty acids is replaced with a phosphate; the molecule is ionised and the phosphate end is water soluble. **Triglycerides** are non-polar and not soluble in water.

2. (a) Solid fats: Saturated fatty acids.
   (b) Oils: Unsaturated fatty acids.

3. The amphipathic nature of phospholipids (with a polar, hydrophilic end and a hydrophobic, fatty acid end) causes them to orientate in aqueous solutions so that the hydrophobic 'tails' point in together. Hence the bilayer nature of phospholipid membranes.

4. (a) Saturated fatty acids contain the maximum number of hydrogen atoms, whereas unsaturated fatty acids contain some double-bonded carbon atoms.
   (b) Saturated fatty acids tend to produce lipids that are solid at room temperature, whereas lipids that contain a high proportion of unsaturated fatty acids tend to be liquid at room temperature.
   (c) The cellular membranes of an Arctic fish could be expected to contain a higher proportion of unsaturated fatty acids than those of a tropical fish species. This would help them to remain fluid at low temperatures.

5. (a) and (b) any of the following:
   • Male and female sex hormones (testosterone, progesterone, oestrogen): regulate reproductive physiology and sexual development.
   • Cortisol: glucocorticoid required for normal carbohydrate metabolism and response to stress.
   • Aldosterone: acts on the kidney to regulate salt (sodium and potassium) balance.
   • Cholesterol is a sterol lipid and, while not a steroid itself, is a precursor to several steroid hormones and a component of membranes.

6. (a) Energy: Fats provide a compact, easily stored source of energy. Energy yield per gram on oxidation is twice that of carbohydrate.
   (b) Water: Metabolism of lipids releases water. **Note**: oxidation of triglycerides releases twice as much water as carbohydrate.
   (c) Insulation: Heat does not dissipate easily through fat therefore thick fat insulates against heat loss.

The Structure of Membranes (page 93)

1. (a) Membranes are composed of a phospholipid bilayer in which are embedded proteins, glycoproteins, and glycolipids. The structure is relatively fluid and the proteins are able to move within this fluid matrix.

   (b) This model accounts for the properties we observe in cellular membranes: its **fluidity** (how its shape is not static and how its components move within the membrane, relative to one-another) and its **mosaic nature** (the way in which the relative proportions of the membrane components, i.e. proteins, glycoproteins, glycolipids etc, can vary from membrane to membrane). The fluid mosaic model also accounts for how membranes can allow for the selective passage of materials (through protein channels for example) and how they enable cell-cell recognition (again, as a result of membrane components such as glycoproteins).

2. Membranes perform numerous diverse roles. The plasma membrane forms the outer limit of the cell and contains the proteins that confer cellular recognition. It also controls the entry and exit of materials into and out of the cell. Intracellular membranes keep the cytoplasm separate from the extracellular spaces and provide compartments within cells for localisation of metabolic (enzymatic) reactions. They also provide a surface for the attachment of the enzymes involved in metabolism.

3. (a) Any of: Golgi apparatus, mitochondria, chloroplasts, endoplasmic reticulum (rough or smooth), nucleus, vacuoles, lysosomes.

   (b) Depends on choice: Generally the membrane's purpose is to compartmentalise the location of enzymatic reactions, to control the entry and exit of substances that the organelle operates on, and/or to provide a surface for enzyme attachment.

4. (a) Cholesterol lies between the phospholipids and prevents close packing. It thus functions to keep membranes more fluid. The greater the amount of cholesterol in the membrane the greater its fluidity.

   (b) At temperatures close to freezing, high proportions of membrane cholesterol is important in keeping membranes fluid and functioning.

5. (a)-(c) in any order: Oxygen, food (glucose), minerals and trace elements, water.

6. (a) Carbon dioxide   (b) Nitrogenous wastes

7.

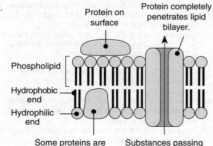

Protein on surface

Protein completely penetrates lipid bilayer.

Phospholipid

Hydrophobic end

Hydrophilic end

Some proteins are embedded in the lipid bilayer.

Substances passing straight through channel provided by the protein.

The Role of Membranes in Cells (page 95)

1. (a) Compartments within cells allow specific metabolic pathways in the cell to be localised. This achieves greater efficiency of cell function and restricts potentially harmful reactions and substances (e.g. hydrogen peroxide) to specific areas.

   (b) Greater membrane surface area provides a greater area over which membrane-bound reactions can occur. This increases the speed and efficiency with which metabolic reactions can take place.

2. (a) Glycoproteins and glycolipids act as cell identity markers so that self and non-self cells can be recognised. Glycolipids also help cells to aggregate in the formation of tissues.

   (b) Channel and carrier proteins facilitate selective transport of substances through the membrane. They can help to speed up the transport of substances into and out of the cell, especially for enzymatic reactions requiring a steady supply of substrate and constant removal of end-product, e.g. ADP supply to the mitochondrion during cellular respiration).

3. Cholesterol can regulate the entry or exit of substances by acting as a selective plug, allowing some substances but not others to enter or leave the cell.

4. (a) Lipid soluble molecules pass easily through the phospholipid bilayer by dissolving in it. Lipid insoluble substances cannot pass directly into the bilayer (they must move through channels).

   (b) Lipid soluble substances pass very rapidly into cells (many drugs are lipid soluble). Lipid insoluble molecules must pass through protein channels (either by facilitated diffusion or active transport).

Active and Passive Transport (page 97)

1. **Passive transport** requires no energy; materials follow a concentration gradient. In contrast, **active transport** directly or indirectly uses energy (ATP) to move materials against their concentration gradient.

2. Gases moving by diffusion: oxygen, carbon dioxide.

3. Any of: Cells in the digestive (exocrine) glands of the stomach, pancreas, upper small intestine (duodenum); endocrine glands (e.g. adrenal glands); salivary glands.

4. (a) Protozoan: *Amoeba, Paramecium*

   (b) A food vacuole develops at the end of the oral groove in *Paramecium* and is pinched off to circulate within the cell. In *Amoeba*, the pseudopodia engulf a food particle and a vacuole is formed where the membrane pinches off after the particle is engulfed.

   (c) Human cell: Phagocyte (phagocytic leucocyte).

Diffusion (page 98)

1. (a) Large surface area   (b) Thin membrane

2. Concentration gradients are maintained by (any one of): Constant use or transport away of a substance on one side of a membrane (e.g. use of ADP in mitochondria). Production of a substance on one side of a membrane (e.g. production of CO_2 by respiring cells).

3. Ionophores allow the preferential passage of some molecules but not others.

Osmosis and Water Potential (page 99)
1. Zero

2. and 3. (a)-(c):

(a)
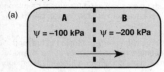
A | B
$\psi = -100$ kPa | $\psi = -200$ kPa

(b)
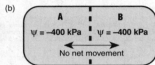
A | B
$\psi = -400$ kPa | $\psi = -400$ kPa
No net movement

(c)
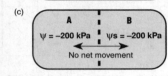
A | B
$\psi = -200$ kPa | $\psi s = -200$ kPa
No net movement

4. (a) Hypotonic
   (b) Fluid replacements must induce the movement of water into the cells and tissues (which are dehydrated and therefore have a more negative water potential than the drink). **Note:** Many sports drinks are isotonic. Depending on the level of dehydration involved, these drinks are more effective when diluted.

5. *Paramecium* is hypertonic to the surrounding freshwater environment and water constantly flows into the cell. This must be continually pumped out (by contractile vacuoles).

6. (a) Pressure potential generated within plant cells provides the turgor necessary for keeping unlignified plant tissues supported.
   (b) Without cell turgor, soft plant tissues (soft stems and flower parts for example) would lose support and wilt. Note that some tissues are supported by structural components such as lignin.

7. Animal cells are less robust than plant cells against changes in net water content: Excess influx will cause bursting and excess loss causes crenulation.

8. (a) Water will move into the cell and it will burst (lyse).
   (b) The cell would lose water and the plasma membrane would crinkle up (crenulate).
   (c) Water will move into the cell and it will burst (lyse).

9. Malarial parasite: **Isotonic** to blood.

Ion Pumps (page 101)
1. ATP (directly or indirectly) supplies the energy to move substances against their concentration gradient.

2. (a) Cotransport describes coupling the movement of a molecule (such as sucrose or glucose) against its concentration gradient to the diffusion of an ion (e.g. H^+ or Na^+) down its concentration gradient. Note: An energy requiring ion exchange pump is used to establish this concentration gradient.

(b) In the gut, a gradient in sodium ions is used to drive the transport of glucose across the epithelium. A Na^+/K^+ pump (requiring ATP) establishes an unequal concentration of Na^+ across the membrane. A specific membrane protein then couples the return of Na^+ down its concentration gradient to the transport of glucose (at a rate that is higher than could occur by diffusion alone).
(c) The glucose then diffuses from the epithelial cells of the gut into the blood stream, where it is transported away. This maintains a low level in the intestinal epithelial cells.

3. Extracellular accumulation of Na^+ (any two of):
   – maintains the gradient that is used to cotransport useful molecules, such as glucose, into cells.
   – maintains cell volume by creating an osmotic gradient that drives the absorption of water
   – establishes and maintains resting potential in nerve and muscle cells
   – provides the driving force for several facilitated membrane transport proteins

Exocytosis and Endocytosis (page 102)
1. **Phagocytosis** is the engulfment of solid material by endocytosis whereas **pinocytosis** is the uptake of liquids or fine suspensions by endocytosis.

2. Phagocytosis examples (any of):
   • Feeding in *Amoeba* by engulfment of material using cytoplasmic extensions called pseudopodia. • Ingestion of old red blood cells by Kupffer cells in the liver. • Ingestion of bacteria and cell debris by neutrophils and macrophages (phagocytic white blood cells).

3. Exocytosis examples (any of):
   • Secretion of substances from specialised secretory cells in multicellular organisms, e.g. hormones from endocrine cells, digestive secretions from exocrine cells. • Expulsion of wastes from unicellular organisms, e.g. *Paramecium* and *Amoeba* expelling residues from food vacuoles.

4. Any type of cytosis (unlike diffusion) is an active process involving the use of ATP. Low oxygen inhibits oxidative metabolism and lowers the energy yield from the respiration of substrates (ATP availability drops).

5. (a) **Oxygen:** Diffusion.
   (b) **Cellular debris:** Phagocytosis.
   (c) **Water:** Osmosis.
   (d) **Glucose:** Facilitated diffusion.

Cholera (page 103)
1. The bacterium *Vibrio cholerae*.

2. If untreated, the copious diarrhoea can quickly lead to severe dehydration and a consequent collapse of all body systems (particularly kidney and heart failure).

3. Treatment with ORS provides replaces the electrolytes lost with the diarrhoea as well as the water. Glucose or sucrose in the ORS enhance electrolytes absorption. Drinking water alone does not address electrolyte loss.

4. When glucose is added to an ORS symptoms can worsen initially because the presence of sugars in the gut can make the diarrhoea worse (as a result of

osmotic withdrawal of water into the gut lumen). This can cause people to stop treatment even though overall hydration is improved and electrolyte loss is reduced.

5. As with any trials, there is a risk that a new product may worsen the diarrhoea or have unexpected undesirable side effects. If a new product is ineffectual, there is a risk that the inadequacy of the treatment could be life threatening. The ethics of trials are especially fraught when the trials involve one group of patients receiving a placebo (no effect) or a less effective treatment (these are used to measure the extent to which the new product is better).

Introduction to Gas Exchange (page 105)

1. **Cellular respiration** refers to the production of ATP through the oxidation of glucose. **Gas exchange** refers to the way in which respiratory gases (oxygen and carbon dioxide) are exchanged with the environment. Oxygen is required to drive the reactions of cellular respiration. Carbon dioxide is a waste product.

2. (a) Moist so that gases can dissolve and diffuse across.
   (b) Large surface area to provide for a large amount of gas exchange (to meet the organism's needs).
   (c) Thin membrane that does not present a large barrier to diffusion of gases. This provides a surface across which gases easily diffuse.

3. The rate of diffusion across the gas exchange surface will be more rapid when membrane surface area or concentration difference across the membrane increases and/or membrane thickness decreases.

Breathing in Humans (page 106)

1. **Breathing** ventilates the lungs, renewing the supply of fresh (high oxygen) air while expelling high carbo dioxide air (CO_2 gained as a result of gas exchanges in the tissues).

2. (a) **Quiet breathing**: External intercostal muscles and diaphragm contract. Lung space increases and air flows into the lungs (inspiration). Inflation is detected and breath in ends. Expiration occurs through elastic recoil of the ribcage and lung tissue (air flows passively out to equalise with outside air pressure).
   (b) During forced or **active breathing**, muscular contraction is involved in both the inspiration and the expiration (expiration is not passive).

3. Water vapour

4. The elasticity of the lung tissue enable natural recoil of the lungs during quiet breathing so that expiration is a passive process not requiring energy.

5. Blood pH is a good indicator of high carbon dioxide levels, since increased CO_2 levels cause blood pH to fall. This indicates a need to increase respiratory rate to remove the CO_2 (and obtain more oxygen).

The Human Respiratory System (page 107)

1. (a) The structural arrangement (lobes, each with its own bronchus and dividing many times before terminating in numerous alveoli) provides an immense surface area for gas exchange.

(b) Gas exchange takes place in the alveoli.

2. The respiratory membrane is the layered junction between the alveolar cells, the endothelial cells of the capillaries, and their associated basement membranes. It provides a surface across which gases can freely move.

3. Surfactant reduces the surface tension of the lung tissue and counteracts the tendency of the alveoli to recoil inward and stick together after each expiration.

4. Completed table as below:

	Region	Cartilage	Ciliated epithelium	Goblet cells (mucus)	Smooth muscle	Connective tissue
❶	Trachea	✓	✓	✓	✓	✓
❷	Bronchus	✓	✓	✓	✓	✓
❸	Bronchioles	gradually lost	✓	✓	✓	✓
❹	Alveolar duct	✗	✗	✗	✓	✓
❺	Alveoli	✗	✗	✗	very little	✓

5. Respiratory distress syndrome: The lack of surfactant and high surface tension in the alveoli result in the collapse of the lungs to an uninflated state after each breath. Breathing is difficult and laboured, oxygen delivery is inadequate and, if untreated, death usually follows in a few hours.

Measuring Lung Function (page 109)

1. (a) Taller people generally have larger lung volumes and capacities.
   (b) Males have larger lung volumes and capacities than females.
   (c) After adulthood, lung volume and capacity declines with age. Children have smaller lung volumes and lung capacities than adults.

2. (a) Forced volume is a more useful indicator of impairment of lung function than a tidal volume because people use only a small proportion of their lung volume in normal breathing.
   (b) Spirometry can be used to measure the extent of recovery of lung function after treatment.

3. (a) Tidal volume   vol: 0.5 dm^3
   (b) Expiratory reserve volume   vol: 1.0 dm^3
   (c) Residual volume   vol: 1.2 dm^3
   (d) Inspiratory capacity   vol: 3.8 dm^3
   (e) Vital capacity   vol: 4.8 dm^3
   (f) Total lung capacity   vol: 6.0 dm^3

4. **G**: Tidal volume is increasing as a result of exercise.

5. PV: 15 x 400 = 6000 cm^3 or 6 dm^3

6. (a) During strenuous exercise, PV increases markedly.
   (b) Increased PV is achieved as a result of an increase in both breathing rate and tidal volume.

7. (a) There is 90X more CO_2 in exhaled air than in inhaled air (3.6 ÷ 0.04).
   (b) The CO_2 is the product of cellular respiration in the tissues. **Note**: Some texts give a value of 4.0% for exhaled air (100X the CO_2 content of inhaled air).

(c) The dead space air is not involved in gas exchange therefore retains a higher oxygen content than the air that leaves the alveoli air. This raises the oxygen content of the expired air.

Gas Transport in Humans (page 111)

1. (a) Oxygen is high in the lung alveoli and in the capillaries leaving the lung.
   (b) Carbon dioxide is high in the capillaries leaving the tissues and in the cells of the body tissues.

2. Haemoglobin can bind oxygen reversibly, so it can take up oxygen when the oxygen pressures are high (lungs), and carry oxygen to where it is required (the tissues) and release it.

3. (a) Because CO binds so strongly, it quickly occupies all the binding sites of the haemoglobin molecules so that there is very little oxygen carried. The tissues become oxygen deprived and die.
   (b) The blood of smokers has CO in it (from cigarette smoke) and therefore has a much lower oxygen carrying capacity.

Review of Lung Function (page 112)

1. (a) Nasal cavity   (i) Asthma
   (b) Oral cavity   (ii) Emphysema
   (c) Trachea   (iii) Pulmonary tuberculosis
   (d) Lung   (iv) Fibrosis
   (e) Terminal bronchiole
   (f) Alveoli
   (g) Diaphragm

2. A = Inspiratory reserve volume   vol: $3.3 \, dm^3$
   B = Inspiratory capacity   vol: $3.8 \, dm^3$
   C = Tidal volume   vol: $0.5 \, dm^3$
   D = Expiratory reserve volume   vol: $1.0 \, dm^3$
   E = Residual volume   vol: $1.2 \, dm^3$

Respiratory Diseases (page 113)

1. Obstructive lung diseases are those in which the air cannot reach the gas exchange region of the lung, as occurs as a result of airway constriction (asthma), excess mucus (bronchitis), or reduced lung elasticity (emphysema). Restrictive lung diseases result from scarring of the gas exchange surface (fibrosis) which results in stiffening and lack of lung expansion. Such diseases result from inhalation of dusts (e.g. coal dust).

2. (a) In a chronic obstructive pulmonary disease, the FEV_1 is reduced disproportionately more than the FVC resulting in an FEV_1/FVC ratio less than 70%.
   (b) Although the FEV_1/FVC ratio is reduced in asthmatics, there will be an improvement in the ratio towards the normal range (80%+) after treatment.
   (c) In a restrictive lung disease, both FEV1 and the FVC are compromised equally, so even though measures of lung function indicate impairment the FEV1/FVC ratio remains high.

3. Restrictive lung diseases, such as **fibrosis**, impair lung function because the gas exchange surface becomes scarred, less flexible, and thicker. This reduces the amount of alveolar expansion possible and reduces the diffusion efficiency across the gas exchange surface.

4. Many restrictive diseases are caused by inhalation of dusts and pollutants associated with particular occupations, e.g. asbestos workers, coal miners, beryllium miners, cement workers etc.

5. In an asthma attack, histamine is released from sensitised mast cells. The histamine causes airway constriction, accumulation of fluid and mucus, and inability to breathe.

Diseases Caused by Smoking (page 115)

1. Long-term smoking results in increased production of mucus (in an attempt to trap and rid the lungs of smoke particles). This lung tissue is irritated and a cough develops associated with removing the excess mucus. The smoke particles indirectly destroy the alveolar walls, leading to coalescing of the alveoli and a substantial loss of lung surface area. The toxins in the smoke and tar damage the DNA of cells and lead to cancerous cells and tumours.

2. (a) **Tars**: Cause chronic irritation of the respiratory system and are also carcinogenic
   (b) **Nicotine**: Addictive component of tobacco smoke
   (c) **Carbon monoxide**: Markedly reduces the oxygen carrying capacity of the blood by binding to haemoglobin and forming a stable carboxy-haemoglobin compound. CO has a very high affinity for Hb (higher than that of oxygen) and will preferentially occupy oxygen binding sites. It is released only slowly for the body.

3. (a) **Emphysema**: Increasing shortness of breath (which becomes increasingly more severe until it is present even at rest). Chest becomes barrel shaped (associated with air being trapped in the outer part of the lungs). Often accompanied by a chronic cough and wheeze (caused by the distension (damage and coalescing) of the alveoli). **Note**: Chronic bronchitis and emphysema are often together called chronic obstructive lung disease.
   (b) **Chronic bronchitis**: A condition in which sputum (phlegm) is coughed up on most days during at least three consecutive months in at least two consecutive years. The disease results in widespread narrowing and obstruction of the airways in the lungs and often occurs with or contributes to emphysema.
   (c) **Lung cancer**: Impaired lung function; coughing up blood, chest pain, breathlessness, and death.

4. The evidence linking cigarette smoking to increased incidence of respiratory and cardiovascular diseases and cancer is clear and convincing. The incidence of these diseases in smokers is much higher than in non-smokers even when other factors such as age and familial tendency are considered. For example, deaths from lung cancer in the UK are five times higher in smokers than in non-smokers. These differences are large enough to be statistically significant. Importantly, the evidence linking smoking to the incidence of specific diseases comes from many different sources and is not conflicting.

Tuberculosis (page 117)

1. (a) Inhalation of the TB pathogen results in a defence response from the lung macrophages, leading to

formation of tubercles (nodules) in the lung tissue which can rupture through the alveolar walls to release infective bacteria into the airways. These regions are replaced by scarring and areas of necrotic (dying) tissue which are ineffective for gas exchange. Fluid accumulation is associated with this. The greater the extent of infection, the more congestion, scarring and necrosis, and the greater the amount of gas exchange surface lost.

(b) TB is transmitted by airborne droplets, which are coughed or sneezed out following the rupture of tubercles, which releases bacilli into the airways.

2. The body's immune response is capable of walling-off the bacteria in nodules (tubercles). In this dormant state, the bacteria do not have the capacity to cause disease symptoms and the person is not infectious.

The Human Heart (page 119)

1. (a) Pulmonary artery (e) Aorta
   (b) Vena cava (f) Pulmonary vein
   (c) Right atrium (g) Left atrium
   (d) Right ventricle (h) Left ventricle

Positions of heart valves

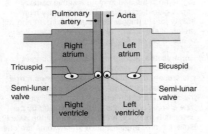

2. **Valves** prevent the blood from flowing the wrong way through the heart and help regulate filling of the chambers.

3. (a) The heart has its own coronary blood supply to meet the high oxygen demands of the heart tissue.
   (b) There must be a system within the heart muscle itself to return deoxygenated blood and waste products of metabolism back to the right atrium.

4. If blood flow to a particular part of the heart is restricted or blocked (because of blocked blood vessel), the part of the heart muscle supplied by that vessel will die, leading to a heart attack or infarction.

5. A: arterioles   B: venules
   C: arterioles   D: capillaries

6. (a) The **pulse pressure** is the difference between the systolic pressure and the diastolic pressure.
   (b) Pulse pressure between the aorta and the capillaries will decrease (because of the increasing resistance met on route).

7. (a) You are recording expansion and recoil of the artery that occurs with each contraction of the left ventricle.
   (b) The best place to take a **pulse** is from the brachial or carotid artery. The blood flow from these arteries (close to the heart) is at a high pressure and still carries the beat or pulse.

Control of Heart Activity (page 121)

1. (a) **Sinoatrial node**: Initiates the cardiac cycle through the spontaneous generation of action potentials.
   (b) **Atrioventricular node**: Delays the impulse.
   (c) **Bundle of His**: Distributes the action potentials over the ventricles (resulting in ventricular contraction).

2. Delaying the impulse at the AVN allows time for atrial contraction to finish before the ventricles contract.

3. (a) Cardiac output
     70 cm^3 X 70 beats per min. = 4900 cm^3 = 4.9 dm^3.
   (b) Trained endurance athletes achieve a high cardiac output primarily through having a very high stroke volume: the heart pumps a lot of blood with each beat. For any given level of exercise, their heart rates are relatively low.

4. (a) **Myogenic**: The heart muscle is capable of rhythmic contraction independently of any external nervous stimulation.
   (b) **Evidence**: When the heart is removed from its nervous supply (if provided with adequate oxygen, ions, and fluids) will continue to beat.

5. Heavy exercise alters blood composition (lowering blood oxygen and pH) and increases venous return to the heart. These changes stimulate the accelerator centre in the medulla either directly (via blood composition) or via sensory impulses from stretch receptors in the vena cavae and atrium (venous return). The accelerator centre responds by sympathetic stimulation of the heart (via the cardiac nerve and release of noradrenaline) bringing about increased rate and force of heart contraction.

6. (a) Increased arterial flow (in aorta and carotid arteries).
   (b) Stretch receptors in carotid sinus and aorta detect an increase in arterial flow and send afferent impulses to the inhibitory centre in the medulla. The inhibitory centre mediates a decrease in heart rate via the vagus nerve (the carotid and aortic reflexes). There is a subsequent decrease in cardiac output and arterial blood pressure.

7. (a) and (b) any of the following in any order:
   – Aortic pressure receptors (baroreceptors) in the wall of the aortic arch respond to increased arterial blood flow in the aorta.
   – Carotid baroreceptors in the carotid sinus respond to increased arterial flow in the carotid artery.
   – Baroreceptors in the vena cava and the right atrium respond to increased venous return (mediates an increase in heart rate - the Bainbridge reflex).

8. (a) Individuals have different tolerances to the same level of a substance (also depends on their previous intakes of other substances such as coffee). Different body mass will affect the response also.
   (b) Controls should drink an energy drink that does not contain guarana.

The Cardiac Cycle (page 123)

1. (a) QRS complex   (b) T   (c) P

2. During the period of electrical recovery the heart muscle cannot contract. This ensures that the heart has an enforced rest and will not fatigue, nor accumulate lactic acid (as occurs in working skeletal muscle).

3. Extra text removed and letter answers have been placed for each cycle.

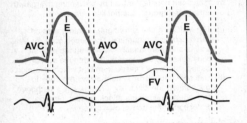

Review of the Human Heart (page 124)

1. (A) Cardiac nerve (sympathetic nerve is acceptable).
   (B) Baroreceptors in the vena cava and right atrium.
   (C) Vagus nerve (parasympathetic nerve is acceptable).
   (D) Aortic baroreceptors.
   (1) Sinoatrial node (SAN).
   (2) Atrioventricular node (AVN).
   (3) Bundle of His (atrioventricular bundle).
   (4) Right ventricle.
   (5) Pulmonary artery.
   (6) Left atrium.
   (7) Purkinje fibres.
   (8) Left ventricle.

2. A = Contraction of the atria.
   B = Contraction of the ventricles.
   C = Relaxation and recovery of ventricles.

3. Use of an artificial pacemaker to regulate heart rhythm.

Exercise and Blood Flow (page 125)

1. Answers for missing values are listed from top to bottom under the appropriate heading:

	At rest (% of total)	Exercise (% of total)
Heart	4.0	4.2
Lung	2.0	1.1
Kidneys	22.0	3.4
Liver	27.0	3.4
Muscle	15.0	70.2
Bone	5.0	1.4
Skin	6.0	10.7
Thyroid	1.0	0.3
Adrenals	0.5	0.1
Other	3.5	1.0

2. The heart beats faster and harder to increase the volume of blood pumped per beat and the number of beats per minute (increased blood flow).

3. (a) Blood flow increases approximately 3.5 times.
   (b) Working tissues require more oxygen and nutrients than can be delivered by a resting rate of blood flow. Therefore the rate of blood flow (delivery to the tissues) must increase during exercise.

4. (a) Thyroid and adrenal glands, as well as the tissues other than those defined in the table, show no change in absolute rate of blood flow.
   (b) This is because they are not involved in exercise and do not require an increased blood flow. However, they do need to maintain their usual blood supply and cannot tolerate an absolute decline.

5. (a) Skeletal muscles (increases 16.7X), skin (increases 6.3X), and heart (increases 3.7X)
   (b) These tissues and organs are all directly involved in the exercise process and need a greater rate of supply of oxygen and nutrients. Skeletal muscles move the body, the heart must pump a greater volume of blood at a greater rate and the skin must help cool the body to maintain core temperature.

6. Heart size increases because (like any muscle) it gets bigger with work. The larger size also means it pumps a greater volume of blood more efficiently.

7. Endurance athletes have a smaller body weight.

8. With each stroke, the heart pumps a larger volume of blood. Less energy is expended in pumping the same volume of blood.

9. A lower resting heart rate means that for most of the time, the heart is not working as hard as in someone with a higher resting heart rate.

Cardiovascular Disease (page 127)

1. As it develops, **atherosclerosis** leads to blockage and obstruction of blood flow in the affected artery. The region of heart muscle normally supplied by the affected artery dies, causing severe pain and irregularity in the heart beat. Damage to the heart muscle may be so severe, it may lead to heart failure.

2. (a) Atheroma increases the risk of aneurysm because it weakens the arterial walls and, combined with high blood pressure leads to increased risk of the arterial wall ballooning out (aneurysm) and rupturing.
   (b) Plaque material from an atheroma can detach from the artery wall and enter the circulation where it can bock small vessels and lead to blood clot formation (thrombosis) and consequently, stroke.

3. (a) Controllable risk factors for CVD are those that can be altered by changing diet or other lifestyle factors, or by controlling a physiological disease state (e.g. high blood pressure, or high blood cholesterol). Uncontrollable risk factors are those over which no control is possible i.e. genetic predisposition, sex, or age. Note that the impact of uncontrollable factors can be reduced by changing controllable factors.
   (b) Controllable risk factors often occur together because some tend to be causative for others, or at least always associated, e.g. obesity greatly increases the risk of high blood lipids and high blood pressure: all factors increase the risk of CVD.
   (c) Those with several risk factors have a higher chance of developing coronary heart disease (CHD) because the risks are cumulative and add up to pose a greater total risk. As seen in the column chart, the risk of CHD is cumulative and rises by

5-10% approximately with the addition of each of the risk factors indicated. Smoking combined with high HDL cholesterol and diabetes pose the greatest increased risk of CHD.

4. (a) LDL deposits cholesterol on the endothelial lining of blood vessels, whereas HDL transports cholesterol to the liver where it is processed. A high LDL:HDL ratio is more likely to result in CVD because more cholesterol will be deposited on blood vessels and contribute to atherosclerosis.

    (b) The LDL:HDL ratio is a more accurate predictor of heart disease risk than total cholesterol per se.

The Health Benefits of Exercise (page 129)

1. (a) Blood flow rate is increased during exercise through increased rate and force of heart contraction and skeletal muscle contraction, and dilation of blood vessels.

    (b) Physiological effects of regular exercise include: An increase in muscular strength and flexibility, more efficient heart function, improvement in immune function, increased concentration, and higher energy levels.

    (c) These changes in physiology equip the body to handle the usual, everyday events of life with less effort and stress. Ongoing benefits include improved blood flow and more efficient organ function, faster tissue repair, better weight control, improved sleep and stress management, and better immune function. **Note**: These benefits do not extend to over-training, when stresses exceed the health benefits gained from exercise.

2. (a) **Increase in stroke volume and cardiac output**:
    Health benefits: Lower resting heart rate, lower blood pressure and improved cardiovascular performance.
    Physiological mechanism: Increases the volume of blood transported with each beat to and from the working tissues.

    (b) **Increased ventilation efficiency**:
    Health benefits: Regular breathing is easier to sustain with less effort required during periods of activity. Physiological mechanism: Increases the rate of gas exchange (oxygen transported into and carbon dioxide transported out of the blood).

    (c) **Increase in lean muscle and decreased body fat**:
    Health benefits: General increase in level of fitness and muscular performance with the various physiological and psychological benefits that stem from this.
    Physiological mechanism: An increase in the amount of muscle tissue that can be recruited into work and a decrease in the amount of non-active tissue (fat) that must be moved around.

    (d) **Increased muscular strength and endurance**:
    Health benefits: Improved stamina and less chance of injury when exercising.
    Physiological mechanism: Improvements in cardiovascular and ventilation performance and greater resilience during activity.

    (e) **Maintenance of stable, healthy body weight**:
    Health benefits: Decline in the risk of suffering heart disease and other associated illnesses.
    Physiological mechanism: Controls weight by reducing body fat and building muscle and improves the metabolism of food by the body.

3. Irregular or very low intensity exercise does not improve the body's cardiovascular performance or ventilation efficiency because the body is not challenged frequently enough to adapt to the stress of repeated exercise. In fact, irregular exercise may contribute to physiological stress in an unfit individual.

Targets for Defence (page 133)

1. The natural population of (normally non-pathogenic) microbes can benefit the host by preventing overgrowth of pathogens (through competitive exclusion).

2. (a) The MHC is a cluster of tightly linked genes on chromosome 6 in humans. The genes code for MHC antigens that are attached to the surfaces of all body cells and are used by the immune system to distinguish its own tissue from that which is foreign.

    (b) This self-recognition system allows the body to immediately identify foreign tissue, e.g. a pathogen, and mount an immune attack against it for the protection of the body's own tissues.

3. Self-recognition is undesirable:
    – **During pregnancy**. **Note**: Some features of the self-recognition system are disabled to enable growth (to full term) of a foreign body.
    – **During tissue and organ grafts/transplants** from another human (allografting) or a non-human animal (xenografting). **Note**: Such grafts are usually for the purpose of replacing rather than repairing tissue (e.g. grafting to replace damaged heart valves). For these grafts, tissue-typing provides the closest match possible between recipient and donor. The self-recognition system must also be suppressed indefinitely by immunosuppressant drugs.

Blood Group Antigens (page 134)

1. See table below:

Blood type	Antigen	Antibody	Can donate blood to:	Can receive blood from:
A	A	anti-B	A, AB	A, O
B	B	anti-A	B, AB	B, O
AB	A + B	none	AB	A, B, AB, O
O	None	anti-A + anti-B	O, AB, A, B	O

2. (a) Blood typing can eliminate an individual from a group of suspects (i.e. exclude some blood types), but is unlikely to be able to positively identify a criminal. Its forensic use is limited because there are too many people who share a common blood type; the pool of "suspects" would be too large.

    (b) Blood typing can exclude potential fathers in disputed case, but not necessarily prove who is.

    (c) Typing allows blood matching for successful and safe transfusions to replace blood loss in patients.

3. Discovery of the basis of the ABO system allowed the possibility of safe transfusions and greatly improved

survival and recovery after surgery or trauma.

Blood (page 135)

1. **Note**: In some cases, the answers below provide more detail than expected. This is provided as extension.
   (b) Protection against disease:
      Blood component: White blood cells
      Mode of action: Engulf bacteria, mediate immune reactions, and allergic and inflammatory responses.
   (c) Communication between cells, tissues and organs:
      Blood component: Hormones
      Mode of action: Specific chemicals which are carried in the blood to target tissues, where they interact with specific receptors and bring about an appropriate response.
   (d) Oxygen transport:
      Blood component: Haemoglobin molecule of erythrocytes.
      Mode of action: Binds oxygen at the lungs and releases it at the tissues.
   (e) Carbon dioxide transport:
      Blood components: Mainly plasma (most carbon dioxide is carried as bicarbonate in the plasma, a small amount is dissolved in the plasma). Red blood cells (a small amount (10-20%) of carbon dioxide is carried bound to haemoglobin).
      Mode of action: Diffuses between tissues, plasma, and lungs according to concentration gradient.
   (f) Buffer against pH changes:
      Blood components: Haemoglobin molecule of erythrocytes. Plasma bicarbonate and proteins.
      Mode of action: Free hydrogen ions are picked up and carried by the haemoglobin molecule (removed from solution). Plasma bicarbonate can form either carbonic acid by picking up a hydrogen ion (H^+), or sodium bicarbonate by combining with sodium ions. Negatively charged proteins also associate with H^+.
   (g) Nutrient supply:
      Blood component: Plasma
      Mode of action: Glucose is carried in the plasma and is taken up by cells (made available throughout the body to all tissues).
   (h) Tissue repair:
      Blood components: Platelets and leucocytes
      Mode of action: Platelets initiate the cascade of reactions involved in clotting and wound repair. Leucocytes (some types) engulf bacteria and foreign material, preventing or halting infection.
   (i) Transport of hormones, lipids, and fat soluble vitamins:
      Blood component: α-globulins
      Mode of action: α-globulins bind these substances and carry them in the plasma. This prevents them being filtered in the kidneys and lost in the urine.

2. Any of: Presence (WBC) or absence (RBC) of **nucleus**. Colour, reflecting presence (RBC) or absence (WBC) of respiratory pigment, **haemoglobin**. **Shape and size** (smaller, dish shaped RBCs vs larger, rounded WBCs. **Mitochondria** present in WBCs, absent in RBCs.

3. (a) Lack of a nucleus allows more space inside the cell to carry Hb (hence greater O_2 carrying capacity).
   (b) Lack of mitochondria forces the red blood cells to metabolise anaerobically so that they do not consume the oxygen they are carrying.

4. (a) Elevated eosinophil count: Allergic response such

as hay fever or asthma.
   (b) Elevated neutrophil count: Microbial infection.
   (c) Elevated basophil count: Inflammatory response e.g. as a result of an allergy or a parasitic (as opposed to bacterial) infection.
   (d) Elevated lymphocyte count: Infection or response to vaccination.

The Body's Defences (page 137)

1. The **first line of defence** provides non-specific resistance by forming a physical barrier to the entry of pathogens. Chemical secretions from the skin, tears, and saliva also provide antimicrobial activity and help destroy pathogens and wash them away. The **second line of defence** provides non-specific resistance operating inside the body to inhibit or destroy pathogens (irrespective of what type of pathogen is involved). Whereas the **third line of defence** provides specific defence resistance against particular pathogens once they have been identified by the immune system (antibody production and cell-mediated immunity).

2. **Specific resistance** refers to defence against particular (identified) pathogens. It involves a range of specific responses to the pathogen concerned (antibody production and cell-mediated immunity). In contrast, **non-specific resistance** refers to defence against any type of pathogen.

3. The leucocytes involved in the second line of defence are the macrophages and the granulocytes (eosinophils, neutrophils, and basophils), so-called because of the granular appearance of their cytoplasm.
   (a) Macrophages: phagocytic, actively engulfing and destroying foreign material (e.g. bacteria).
   (b) Eosinophils produce antimicrobial substances, including proteins toxic to certain parasites. They also show some phagocytic properties.
   (c) Basophils release heparin (an anticoagulant) and histamine which is involved in inflammation and allergic reactions.
   (d) Neutrophils are phagocytic, actively engulfing and destroying foreign material.

4. Functional role for (b)–(i) as follows:
   (b) **Phagocytosis** destroys pathogens directly by engulfing them.
   (c) Sticky **mucus** traps pathogens and **cilia** move the trapped microbes towards the mouth and nostrils.
   (d) Some secretions (sebum) have a pH unfavourable to microbial growth. The pH of **gastric juice** is low enough to kill microbes directly. Other secretions (**tears, saliva**) wash microbes away, preventing them settling on surfaces, sweat contains an enzyme that destroys some types of bacterial cell walls, **urine** flushes microbes from the urinary tract.
   (e) Antimicrobial properties of some proteins (e.g. **interferon**) prevent multiplication of microbes (especially viruses).
   (f) Produced against specific pathogens, **antibodies** bind and destroy pathogens or their toxins.
   (g) **Fever** raises general body temperature and metabolic rate which speeds up the blood flow and the rate of delivery of white blood cells to the site of infection. Fever also intensifies the effect of interferon.
   (h) **T cells** recognise and destroy target pathogens

on contact. Other T cells assist by regulating the activity of other lymphocytes.

(i) Heat inhibits the activity of the pathogens at the site of infection. Swelling and pain help to confine the infection to a limited area by limiting movement, increased blood flow speeds up the delivery of white blood cells and speeds healing.

5. With few T cells, the body lacks an effective cell mediated immune system and responds poorly to opportunistic pathogens that get past the first defences.

Blood Clotting and Defence (page 139)

1. (a) Prevents bleeding and invasion of bacteria.
   (b) Aids in the maintenance of blood volume.

2. (a) Injury exposes collagen fibres to the blood.
   (b) Chemicals make the surrounding platelets sticky.
   (c) Clumping forms an immediate plug of platelets preventing blood loss.
   (d) Fibrin clot traps red blood cells and reinforces the seal against blood loss.

3. (a) Clotting factors catalyse the conversion of prothrombin to thrombin, the active enzyme that catalyses the production of fibrin.
   (b) If the clotting factors were present all the time, the clotting could not be contained and the blood would clot when it should not.

4. (a) and (b) provided below. The first is the obvious answer, but there are disorders associated with the absence of each of the twelve clotting factors:
   (a) Classic haemophilia.
   (b) Clotting factor VIII (anti-haemophiliac factor).

   (a) Haemophilia B (Christmas disease).
   (b) Clotting factor IX (Christmas factor).

The Action of Phagocytes (page 140)

1. Neutrophils, eosinophils, macrophages.

2. By looking at the ratio of white blood cells to red blood cells (not involved in the immune response). An elevated white blood cell count (specifically a high neutrophil count) indicates microbial infection.

3. Microbes may be able to produce toxins that kill phagocytes directly. Others can enter the phagocytes, completely filling them and preventing them functioning or remaining dormant and resuming activity later.

Inflammation (page 141)

1. (a) **Increased diameter and permeability of blood vessels**. Purpose: Increases blood flow and delivery of leucocytes to the area. Aids removal of destroyed microbes or their toxins. Allows defensive substances to leak into the tissue spaces.
   (b) **Phagocyte migration and phagocytosis**. Purpose: To directly attack and destroy invading microbes and foreign substances.
   (c) **Tissue repair**. Purpose: Replaces damaged cells and tissues, restoring the integrity of the area.

2. Phagocytic features: Ability to squeeze through capillary walls (amoeboid movement), and ability to engulf material by phagocytosis.

3. Histamines and prostaglandins attract phagocytes to the site of infection.

4. **Pus** is the accumulated debris of infection (dead phagocytes, damaged tissue, and fluid). It accumulates at the site of infection where the defence process is most active.

Fever (page 142)

1. The high body temperature associated with fever intensifies the action of interferon (a potent antiviral substance). Fever also increases metabolism, which is associated with increased blood flow. These changes increase the rate at which white blood cells are delivered to the site of infection and help to speed up the repair of tissues. The release of interleukin-1 during fever helps to increase the production of T cell lymphocytes and speeds up the immune response.

2. **1:** Macrophage ingests a microbe and destroys it.
   2: The release of endotoxins from the microbe induces the macrophage to produce interleukin-1 which is released into the blood.
   3: Interleukin-1 travels in the blood to the hypothalamus of the brain where it stimulates the production of large amounts of prostaglandins.
   4: Prostaglandins cause resetting of the thermostat to a higher temperature, causing fever.

The Immune System (page 143)

1. (a) **Humoral immune system**: Production of antibodies against specific antigens. The antibodies disable circulating antigens.
   (b) **Cell-mediated immune system**: Involves the production of T cells which destroy pathogens or their toxins by direct contact or by producing substances that regulate the activity of other cells in the immune system.

2. In the bone marrow (adults) or liver (foetuses).

3. (a) Bone marrow   (b) Thymus

4. (a) **Memory cells**: Retain an antigen memory. They can rapidly differentiate into antibody- producing plasma cells if they encounter the same antigen again.
   (b) **Plasma cells**: Secrete antibodies against antigens (very rapid rate of antibody production).
   (c) **Helper T cells**: Activate cytotoxic T cells and other helper T cells. Also needed for B cell activation.
   (d) **Suppressor T cells**: Regulate the immune system response by turning it off when antigens disappear.
   (e) **Delayed hypersensitivity T cells**: Cause inflammation in allergic responses and are responsible for rejection of transplanted tissue.
   (f) **Cytotoxic T cells**: Destroy target cells on contact (by binding and lysing cells).

5. **Immunological memory**: The result of the differentiation of B cells after the first exposure to an antigen. Those B cells that differentiate into long lived memory cells are present to react quickly and vigorously in the event of a second infection.

Antibodies (page 145)

1. **Antibodies** are proteins produced in response to antigens; they recognise and bind antigens. **Antigens** are foreign substances (often proteins) that promote the formation of antibodies (invoke an immune response).

2. (a) The immune system must be able to recognise self from non-self so that it can recognise foreign material (and destroy it) and its own tissue (and not destroy it).
   (b) During development, any B cells that react to the body's own antigens are selectively destroyed. This process leads to self tolerance.
   (c) Autoimmune disease (disorder).
   (d) Any two of: Grave's disease (thyroid enlargement), rheumatoid arthritis (primarily joint inflammation), insulin-dependent diabetes mellitus (caused by immune destruction of the insulin-secreting cells in the pancreas), haemolytic anaemia (premature destruction of red blood cells), and probably multiple sclerosis (destruction of myelin around nerves).

3. Antibodies inactivate pathogens in four main ways: **Neutralisation** describes the way in which antibodies bind to viral binding sites and bacterial toxins and stop their activity. Antibodies may also **inactivate particulate antigens**, such as bacteria, by sticking them together in clumps. Soluble antigens may be bound by antibodies and fall out of solution (**precipitation**) so that they lose activity. Antibodies also activate **complement** (a defence system involving serum proteins), tagging foreign cells so that they can be recognised and destroyed.

4. (a) **Phagocytosis**: Antibodies promote the formation of inactive clumps of foreign material that can easily be engulfed and destroyed by a phagocytic cell.
   (b) **Inflammation**: Antibodies are involved in activation of complement (the defence system involving serum proteins which participate in the inflammatory response and other immune system activities).
   (c) **Bacterial cell lysis**: Antibodies are involved in tagging foreign cells for destruction and in the activation of complement (the defence system involving serum proteins which participate in the lysis of foreign cells).

Antigenic Variability in Pathogens (page 147)

1. (a) The viral genome is contained on 8 short, loosely connected RNA segments. This enables ready exchange of genes between different viral strains and leads to alteration on the protein composition of the H and N glycoprotein spikes.
   (b) The body's immune system acquires antibodies to the H and N spikes (antigens) on the viral surface, but when different variants arise they are not recognised nor detected by the immune system (there is no immunological memory for the newly appearing antigens).

2. An antigenic shift represents the combination of two or more different viral strains in a new subtype with new properties and no immunological history in the population. In contrast, antigenic drifts are much smaller changes that occur continually over time and to which small adjustments (to the flu vaccine or to immune response) are sufficient to provide resistance.

Acquired Immunity (page 148)

1. (a) **Active immunity** is immunity that develops after the body has been exposed to a microbe or its toxins and an immune response has been invoked.
   (b) **Naturally acquired** active immunity arises as a result of exposure to an antigen such as a pathogen, e.g. natural immunity to chickenpox. **Artificially acquired** active immunity arises as a result of vaccination, e.g. any childhood disease for which vaccinations are given: diphtheria, measles, mumps, polio etc.

2. (a) **Passive immunity** describes the immunity that develops after antibodies are transferred from one person to another. In this case, the recipient does not make the antibodies themselves.
   (b) **Naturally acquired** passive immunity arises as a result of antibodies passing from the mother to the foetus/infant via the placenta/breast milk. **Artificially acquired** passive immunity arises as a result of injection with immune serums e.g. in antivenoms.

3. (a) Newborns need to be supplied with maternal antibodies because they have not yet had exposure to the everyday microbes in their environment and must be born with operational defence mechanisms.
   (b) The antibody "supply" is (ideally) supplemented with antibodies in breast milk because it takes time for the infant's immune system to become fully functional. During this time, the supply of antibodies received during pregnancy will decline.

Vaccination (page 149)

1. (a) and (b) See the table at the top of the next page.

2. (a) 280 days
   (b) Antibody levels gradually build to a small peak after 40 days, then gradually decline to very low levels.
   (c) Antibody levels rise very rapidly to a peak (much higher than that achieved after the first injection). Levels then decline slowly over a long period of time.
   (d) The immune system has been "primed" or prepared to respond to the antigen by the first exposure to it (this initial response took a considerable time). When the cells of the immune system receive a second exposure to the same antigen they can respond quickly with rapid production of antibodies.

3. (a) The benefits achieved from childhood vaccination are gained from the protection the children receive from many contagious and potentially life threatening diseases. It is suggested that proper vaccination schedules, if followed, will lead to the elimination of many harmful diseases (as with the eradication of smallpox). It is also suggested that exposure to pathogens in a weakened or inactive form helps to strengthen a growing immune system.
   (b) There is concern about vaccination because of the potentially dangerous side effects that can occur (although these complications are rare). Side effects of concern are very high fevers and seizures (fits) which can lead to nervous system (esp. brain) damage. Those opposed to childhood vaccination also claim that the child's immature immune system is not equipped to deal with the sudden onslaught of different antigens and is adversely affected (perhaps to the extent that the ability to combat common diseases such as colds and flu is compromised).

Vaccination schedule available to children in the United Kingdom		Age / months				Age / years		
Vaccine	Diseases protected from	2	3	4	12-15	3-5	10-14	13-18
DTP (Triple antigen)	Diphtheria, tetanus, pertusis (whooping cough)	✓	✓	✓				
Hib vaccine*	Haemophilus influenzae type b infection*	✓	✓	✓				
OPV (Sabin vaccine)	Poliomyelitis	✓	✓	✓		✓		✓
MMR	Measles, mumps, and rubella (german measles)				✓	✓		
BCG	Tuberculosis						✓	
DT booster	Diphtheria and tetanus					✓		
Td booster	Tetanus, Diphtheria (low strength dose)							✓

Vaccination schedules are also available **for high risk groups** for the following diseases: anthrax, hepatitis A, hepatitis B, influenza, pneumococcal disease, typhoid, varicella (chickenpox), and yellow fever.

* Leads to meningitis in 60% of cases. Other problems include severe respiratory infections and septicemia. Depending on an individual's vaccine tolerance, the Hib vaccine may be conjugated with the DTP vaccine or given as a separate vaccination

4. (a) Asia especially India: Cholera (*Vibrio cholerae*). Note that because this vaccine does not offer reliable protection against different strains, some health professionals are reluctant to provide it.
   (b) Any regions with poor sanitation: Typhoid fever (killed *Salmonella typhi* or live, oral vaccine)
   (c) Tropical areas such as Central and South America and Africa: Yellow fever (attenuated live strain of yellow fever virus).

Types of Vaccine (page 151)

1. (a) **Whole agent vaccine**: Made using entire microorganisms which are killed or weakened and therefore made non-virulent.
   Examples: Vaccines against influenza, measles, mumps, rubella, poliomyelitis, whooping cough.
   (b) **Subunit vaccine**: Made using fragments of a microorganism or a product of the microorganism that is capable of causing an immune response.
   Examples: Vaccines against diphtheria, meningococcal meningitis, tetanus, *Haemophilus influenzae* type b, hepatitis B, whooping cough.
   (c) **Inactivated vaccine**: Made by killing viruses by treating them with formalin or other chemicals.
   Examples: Vaccines against influenza and poliomyelitis (Salk vaccine).
   (d) **Attenuated vaccine**: Made by weakening the virus. Usually this is done by long-term culturing until so many mutations accumulate that the virus becomes non-virulent.
   Examples: Vaccines against mumps, measles, rubella, poliomyelitis (Sabin vaccine).
   (e) **Recombinant vaccine**: Developed with genetic engineering techniques (involving the transfer of DNA between organisms). The gene for some antigenic property of the pathogen (e.g. protein coat) is isolated and spliced into the genome of a benign vector, or a bacterium or yeast which can be cultured to produce large quantities of the antigen.
   Examples: The new vaccines against smallpox and hepatitis B (see 4(b)).
   (f) **Toxoid vaccine**: Bacterial toxins are inactivated with

heat or chemicals. The deactivated toxins (toxoids) retain their antigenic properties and can stimulate the production of antibodies when injected.
   Examples: Vaccines against tetanus and diphtheria.
   (g) **Conjugated vaccine**: Made by combined highly antigenic toxoids with parts of another pathogen that are poorly antigenic (e.g. polysaccharide capsules). This makes the less effective antigen more effective.
   Example: *Haemophilus influenzae* type b vaccine.
   (h) **Acellular vaccine**: Made by fragmenting a whole-agent vaccine and collecting the antigenic portions.
   Example: Vaccine against hepatitis B, newer whooping cough vaccines, typhoid vaccines.

2. **Attenuated viruses** are more effective in the long term because they tend to replicate in the body, and the original dose therefore increases over time. Such vaccines are derived from mutations accumulated over time in a laboratory culture, so there is always a risk that they will back-mutate to a virulent form.

3. Heat kills by denaturing proteins. If the viral proteins are denatured, the virus loses its antigenic properties.

4. (a) They (vaccines made using recombinant methods) are safer because the vaccine is antigenic but not pathogenic. **Note**: Antigenic properties of the pathogen are retained, but there is no risk of developing the disease (as with a live, attenuated vaccine). With recombinant vaccines, the antigen can be produced in large quantities at relatively low cost using large scale culture techniques.
   (b) See the diagrams at the top of the next page (**only one of the two methods is required**).

1

Gene for the antigenic property of the virus (e.g. protein coat) is isolated from the viral genome e.g. smallpox virus (virulent).

2

The gene is spliced into the genome of a non-virulent (benign) viral vector e.g. the generally harmless *Vaccinia* virus.

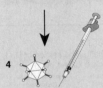

3

The viral vector is cultured in the lab and purified into a vaccine.

4

Viral vector is administered to host. The spliced gene generates the antigenic proteins on the viral surface, promoting a host immune response.

1

Gene for the antigenic property of the virus is isolated from the viral genome e.g. hepatitis B virus (virulent).

2

The gene is spliced into a yeast or bacterial genome (as plasmid DNA).

3

Microbes are cloned and cultured in the laboratory. Each carries a copy of the antigenic gene.

4

Clones manufacture the antigenic protein in culture in large quantities.

5

Protein is purified into a vaccine and injected or given orally. The protein promotes a host response.

Monoclonal Antibodies (page 153)

1. B-lymphocytes.

2. Tumour cells are immortal and, when they fused with B lymphocytes, the resulting hybridomas acquire the ability to be cultured indefinitely.

3. Monoclonal antibodies produced using mouse (foreign) antibodies are likely to cause adverse immune reactions in some people. Newer methods include using genetic engineering techniques to selectively alter existing mouse antibodies to confer more human characteristics. Genetic engineering can also be used to construct chimaeric monoclonal antibodies using variable regions derived from mouse sources and constant regions derived from human sources. These techniques may produce monoclonal antibodies that are more compatible with the human immune system.

4. (a) Detection of bacteria or toxins in perishable food would allow the food to be disposed of rather than consumed and hence the possibility of food poisoning avoided.
   (b) Detection of pregnancy at home would give an instant result, and may circumvent a costly visit to a doctor until a pregnancy was confirmed. For some people, pregnancy detection in the privacy of their home is an attractive option.
   (c) Targeted treatment of cancerous tumours could avoid the need for more invasive or aggressive conventional cancer therapies (which have numerous, often distressing side effects).

Disease and Public Health (page 155)

1. (a) Sporadic increases in incidence associated with seasonal changes.
   (b) Introduction of vaccination against this pathogen.

2. 1990's spike in incidence represents an influenza epidemic and was most likely to be the result of an **antigenic shift** in the virus to which the human population had no immunity.

3. (One of either): Sanitation, medical care, and provision of adequate nutrition are generally poorer in developing countries. The risk factors for the development of lifestyle diseases are more prevalent in developed countries, but the incidence of infectious diseases is lower and treatment for these diseases is better.

4. (a) The incidence of a disease, i.e. the number of new cases per unit time, is an important indicator to how aggressively a disease is spreading through a population. If new cases are appearing very rapidly, the measures required to control the disease (e.g. quarantine) will be different to those required if the disease was spreading slowly (e.g. vaccination).
   (b) The disease incidence data from the SARS outbreak indicated rapid spread from a focal point. This information enabled authorities to decide on an appropriate control programme involving quickly tracing sources of infection, effective quarantine and surveillance, and rapid implementation of hospital procedures and education campaigns aimed at halting spread of infection.

Variation (page 158)

1. Continuous variation is characterised by an exceedingly large number of phenotypic variations (so that a large sample of the population would exhibit a normal distribution for the trait in question). Such traits are determined by a large number of genes and are also frequently influenced by environment, e.g. hand span, weight, skin colour. Discontinuous variation is characterised by a limited number of phenotypic variants. Such traits are determined by a single gene and include features such as chin dimple (present/absent) and blood groups (A, B, AB, O).

2. (a) Wool production: Continuous
   (b) Kernel colour: Continuous
   (c) Blood groups: Discontinuous

(d) Albinism: Discontinuous
(e) Body weight: Continuous
(f) Flower colour: Discontinuous

3. Environmental influence expected on: wool production (a), kernel colour (b), and body weight (e).

4. Student's own plot. Shape of the distribution is dependent on the data collected. The plot should show a **statistically normal distribution** if sample is representative of the population and large enough.
   (a) Calculations based on the student's own data.
   (b) Continuous distribution, normal distribution, or bell shaped curve are all acceptable answers if the data conform to this pattern.
   (c) Polygenic inheritance: Several (two or more) genes are involved in determining the phenotypic trait. Environment may also have an influence, especially if traits such as weight are chosen.
   (d) A large enough sample size (30+), selected randomly provides sufficient unbiased data to fairly indicate the distribution. The larger the sample size, the more closely one would expect the data plot to approximate the normal curve (assuming the sample was drawn from a population with a normal distribution for that attribute).

The Genome (page 161)

1. The **genome** of an organism is a complete haploid set of all chromosomes (i.e. all the genetic material carried by a single representative of each of all chromosome pairs).

2. (a) 5375 bases   (b) 5.375 kb   (c) 0.005375 Mb

3. 1542 bases

4. It is a comparatively small genome, others having 10 to 40 times as much genetic material (e.g. 48.6-190 kb).

Prokaryotic Chromosomes (page 162)

1. (a)-(c) any of in any order:
   – The prokaryotic chromosome is a singular circular chromosome. Eukaryote chromosomes comprise linear DNA packaged with proteins.
   – In prokaryotes, some genes are carried on extra-chromosomal plasmid DNA.
   – The prokaryote chromosome is attached to the plasma membrane and is not enclosed in a nuclear membrane (unlike the eukaryotic chromosomes).
   – Prokaryotic chromosomes consists almost entirely of protein coding genes and their regulatory sequences. Eukaryotic chromosomes contain much intronic DNA that does not code for proteins.

2. Because the DNA in prokaryotes is in direct contact with the cytoplasm, transcription (making mRNA) and translation (protein synthesis) can occur at the same time and the entire process of gene expression occurs much more rapidly than in eukaryotic cells, where the mRNA must leave the nucleus and enter the cytoplasm before translation can begin.

3. The bacterial genome (chromosome) is much smaller than the eukaryotic genome (all chromosomes).

Eukaryote Chromosome Structure (page 163)

1. (a) **DNA**: A long, complex nucleic acid molecule found in the chromosomes of nearly all organisms (some viruses have RNA instead). Provides the genetic instructions (genes) for the production of proteins and other gene products (e.g. RNAs).
   (b) **Chromatin**: Chromosomal material consisting of DNA, RNA, and histone and non-histone proteins. The term is used in reference to chromosomes in the non-condensed state.
   (c) **Histone**: Simple proteins that bind to DNA and help it to coil up during cell division. Histones are also involved in regulating DNA function in some way.
   (d) **Centromere**: A bump or constriction along the length of a chromosome to which spindle fibres attach during cell division. The centromere binds two chromatids together.
   (e) **Chromatid**: One of a pair of duplicated chromosomes produced prior to cell division, joined at the centromere. The terms chromatid and chromosome distinguish duplicated chromosomes before and after division of the centromere.

2. The chromatin (DNA and associated proteins) combine to coil up the DNA into a "super coiled" arrangement. The coiling of the DNA occurs at several levels. The DNA molecule is wrapped around bead-like cores of (8) histone proteins (called nucleosomes), which are separated from each other by linker DNA sequences of about 50 bp. The histones (H1) are responsible for pulling nucleosomes together to form a 30 nm fibre. The chromatin fibre is then folded and wrapped so that it is held in a tight configuration. The different levels of coiling enables a huge amount of DNA to be packed, without tangling, into a very small space in a well organised, orderly fashion.

Nucleic Acids (page 165)

1. (a)-(e) See below (only half of the section of DNA illustrated in the workbook is shown here):

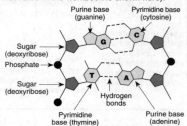

2. (a) The following bases always pair in a normal double strand of DNA:
   guanine with cytosine
   cytosine with guanine
   thymine with adenine
   adenine with thymine
   (b) In mRNA, uracil replaces thymine in pairing with adenine.
   (c) The hydrogen bonds in double stranded DNA hold the two DNA strands together.

3. **Nucleotides** are building blocks of nucleic acids (DNA, RNA). Their precise sequence provides the genetic blueprint for the organism.

4. The **template strand** of DNA is complementary to the **coding strand** and provides the template for the transcription of the mRNA molecule. The coding strand has the same nucleotide sequence as the mRNA (it carries the code), except that thymine in the coding strand substitutes for uracil in the mRNA.

5.

	DNA	RNA
Sugar present	Deoxyribose	Ribose
Bases present	Adenine	Adenine
	Guanine	Guanine
	Cytosine	Cytosine
	Thymine	Uracil
Number of strands	Two (double)	One (single)
Relative length	Long	Short

Creating a DNA Model (page 167)

3. Labels as follows:

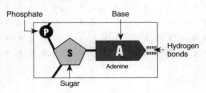

Phosphate Base
Hydrogen bonds
Adenine
Sugar

4. & 5.

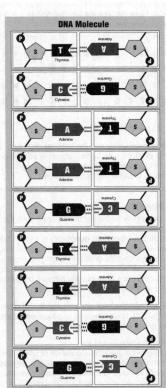

DNA Molecule

6. Factors that prevent a mismatch of nucleotides:
   - The number of hydrogen bond attraction points
   - The size (length) of the base (thymine and cytosine are short, adenine and guanine are long).

   Examples: Cytosine will not match cytosine because the bases are too far apart. Guanine will not match guanine because they are too long to fit side-by-side. Thymine will not match guanine because there is a mismatch in the number and orientation of H bonds.

DNA Molecules (page 171)

1. (a) 95 times more bps (b) 630 times more bps

2. < 2% encodes proteins or structural RNA.

3. (a) Much of the once considered 'junk DNA' has now been found to give rise to functional RNA molecules (many with regulatory functions).
   (b) Complex organisms contain much more of this non-protein-coding DNA which suggests that these sequences contain RNA-only 'hidden' genes that have been conserved through evolution and have a definite role in the development of the organism.

The Genetic Code (page 172)

1. This exercise demonstrates the need for a 3-nucleotide sequence for each codon and the resulting degeneracy in the genetic code.

Amino acid	Codons						No.
Alanine	GCU	GCC	GCA	GCG			4
Arginine	CGU	CGC	CGA	CGG	AGA	AGG	6
Asparagine	AAU	AAC					2
Aspartic Acid	GAU	GAC					2
Cysteine	UGU	UGC					2
Glutamine	CAA	CAG					2
Glutamic Acid	GAA	GAG					2
Glycine	GGU	GGC	GGA	GGG			4
Histidine	CAU	CAC					2
Isoleucine	AUU	AUC	AUA				3
Leucine	UAA	UUG	CUU	CUC	CUA	CUG	6
Lysine	AAA	AAG					2
Methionine	AUG						1
Phenylalanine	UUU	UUC					2
Proline	CCU	CCC	CCA	CCG			4
Serine	UCU	UCC	UCA	UCG	AGU	AGC	6
Threonine	ACU	ACC	ACA	ACG			4
Tryptophan	UGG						1
Tyrosine	UAU	UAC					2
Valine	GUU	GUC	GUA	GUG			4

2. (a) 16 amino acids
   (b) Two-base codons (eg. AT, GG, CG, TC, CA) do not give enough combinations with the 4-base alphabet (A, T, G and C) to code for the 20 amino acids.

3. Many of the codons for a single amino acid vary in the last base only. This would reduce the effect of point mutations, creating new and potentially harmful amino acid sequences in only some instances. **Note**: Only 61 codons are displayed above. The remaining three are **terminator** codons (labelled 'STOP' on the table in the workbook). These are considered the 'punctuation' or controlling codons that mark the end of a gene sequence. The amino acid **methionine** (AUG) is regarded as the 'start' (initiator) codon.

The Simplest Case: Genes to Proteins (page 173)

1. This exercise shows the way in which DNA codes for proteins. Nucleotide has no direct protein equivalent.
   (a) Triplet codes for amino acid.
   (b) Gene codes for polypeptide chain (may be a polypeptide, protein, or RNA product).
   (c) Transcription unit codes for functional protein.

2. (a) **Nucleotides** are made up of: Phosphate, sugar, and one of four bases (adenine, guanine, cytosine, and thymine or uracil).
   (b) **Triplet** is made up of three consecutive nucleotide bases that are read together as a code.
   (c) **Gene** comprises a sequence of triplets, starting with a start code and ending with a termination code.
   (d) **Transcription unit** is made up of two or more genes that together code for a functional protein.

3. Extra detail is provided; essential key words in bold. Steps in making a functional protein:
   • The template strand is made from the DNA coding strand and is transcribed into mRNA (**transcription**).
   • The code on the mRNA is translated into a sequence of amino acids (**translation**), which are linked with peptide bonds to form a polypeptide chain (this may be a functional protein in its own right).
   • The proteins coded by two or more genes come together to form the final functional protein (**folding into functional tertiary structure**).

Meiosis (page 174)

1. In the first division of meiosis, homologous chromosomes pair to form bivalents. Segments of chromosome may be exchanged in crossing over and the homologues then separate (are pulled apart). This division reduces the number of chromosomes in the intermediate cells, so that only one chromosome from each homologous pair is present.

2. In the second division of meiosis, chromatids separate (are pulled apart), but the number of chromsomes stays the same. This is more or less a 'mitotic' division.

3. Mitosis involves a division of the chromatids into two new daughter cells thus maintaining the original number of chromosomes in the parent cell. Meiosis involves a division of the homologous pairs of chromosomes into two intermediary daughter cells thus reducing the diploid number by half. The second stage of meiosis is similar to a mitotic division, but the haploid number is maintained because the chromatids separate.

4. **A** shows metaphase of meiosis I; the homologous pairs of chromosomes are lined up on the cell equator. **B** shows metaphase of meiosis II; the individual chromatids are about to separate.

Crossing Over (page 176)

1. Unexpected combinations of alleles for genes will occur that would not normally be present in gametes.

2. Crossing over provides a source of increased genetic variation amongst individuals in a population. This is important for providing the raw material on which natural selection can act.

Crossing Over Problems (page 177)

Note that each of the problems is independent of the other problems (i.e. they are not a sequence).

1. (a) Gene sequences after crossing over at point 2:

   (b) A, B, and C

2. (a) Gene sequences after crossing over at points 6 & 7.

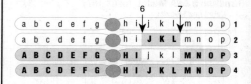

   (b) J, K, and L

3. (a) Gene sequences after crossing over at points 1,3,5, and 7. Note that results for chromatids 2 & 3 are interchangeable.

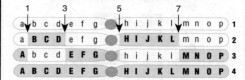

   (b) B, C, D and H, I, J, K, L

4. **Crossing over** increases the amount of mixing of genes to produce new combinations in offspring, therefore increases variation in the gene pool. It counteracts the effect of gene linkage.

Genetic Diversity (page 179)

1. By choosing only particular phenotypes (and therefore genotypes) from which to breed, the average phenotype (and therefore genotype) is altered over successive generations. In this way, the gene pool of the chosen species gradually changes. Artificial selection is a form of directional selection and depends upon the presence of (a certain amount of) genetic variability in the chosen population.

2. Wolves are highly social animals that live in often large groups (packs). Hierarchy and appeasement behaviour bind the group and reduce aggression.

3. Dog breed traits selected for:
   (a) Hunting large game: Good sense of smell, strong bite and strong neck muscles, fearless, aggressive.
   (b) Game fowl hunting: Excellent sense of smell (detection), good eyesight, understanding of need to 'hold', 'point', and retrieve.

(c) Stock control: Must not regard stock as prey (low aggression to stock), obedience (good at taking instructions from farmer, ability to anticipate the behaviour of stock animals and respond to stock movements, bark and use body language to direct stock movement, protect stock from predators.

(d) Family pet: Low level of aggression, playful attributes, friendly disposition.

(e) Guard dog: Aggressive behaviour to strangers, excellent hearing and sense of smell, alert to the arrival of intruders, respond by vigorous barking.

The Founder Effect (page 180)

1.

Mainland	Nos	%		Nos	%
Allele A	48	54.5	Black	11	25
Allele a	40	45.5	Dark	26	59
Total	88	100	Pale	7	16

Island	Nos	%		Nos	%
Allele A	12	75	Black	4	50
Allele a	4	25	Dark	4	50
Total	16	100	Pale	0	0

2. The frequency of the dominant allele (A) is higher on the island population.

3. (a) Plants: Seeds are carried by wind, birds and water.
   (b) Animals: Reach islands largely by 'rafting', whereby animals are carried offshore while clinging to vegetation; some animals survive better than others.
   (c) Non-marine birds: Blown off course and out to sea by a storm. Birds with strong stamina may survive.

4. Genetic drift: Small populations may suffer random, non-directional changes in the frequency of an allele.

Population Bottlenecks (page 181)

1. A sudden decrease in the size of a population can result in a corresponding reduction in genetic variation. This means the population has limited 'genetic resources' to cope with the selection pressures imposed on it. In particular, it is seen as reduced reproductive success and greater sensitivity to disease.

2. Poor genetic diversity means that if one individual is susceptible to a disease, then they are all likely to be vulnerable; a direct result of reduced genetic diversity.

3. With reduced genetic diversity, selection pressures acting on the population are likely to have devastating effects on survival if one trait is found to be unsuited. Since all cheetahs are virtually identical in their traits, if one individual is vulnerable to a selection pressure, then they will all succumb.

Genetic Drift (page 182)

1. **Genetic drift:** Random changes in allele frequencies in small isolated populations, owing to factors other than natural selection. Not all individuals, for various reasons, will be able to contribute their genes to the next generation.

2. Genetic drift reduces the amount of genetic variation in very small populations. Alleles may become eliminated altogether (0%) or become fixed (100%) as the only allele present in the gene pool for a particular gene.

3. Any endangered species with small numbers of individuals remaining: e.g. Puffin, monk seal, European lynx, otter, European beaver, hawksbill turtle, oryx, Siberian tiger (pop. ~500), Chinese tiger (pop. ~250), Sumatran tiger (pop. ~500), humpback whale, grey whale, blue whale.

Selective Breeding in Crop Plants (page 183)

1. A hybrid of inbred lines increases heterozygosity in the offspring. This is associated with a phenotypic response called hybrid vigour, characterised by greater adaptability, survival, growth, and fertility.

2. (a) Cauliflower: flowers
   (b) Kale: leaf
   (c) Broccoli: inflorescence
   (d) Brussels sprout: lateral buds
   (e) Cabbage: apical (terminal) bud
   (f) Kohlrabi: stem (swollen)

3. Any of the following:
   – High yielding crops to maximise crop production.
   – Disease and pest resistant crops lead to increased crop yields and require less pesticide/herbicide application so maximise profit.
   – Fast growing varieties enable the crops to be harvested more quickly and allow more crops to be planted and harvested in a season.

4. (a) Selective breeding for specific traits generally reduces genetic diversity by increasing homozygosity in the offspring. When selection in focussed on specific traits, other phenotypes (therefore genotypes) are rejected and their genes are lost from the gene pool. This is particularly the case when the genes for desirable traits are associated, e.g. a genotype for heavy fruiting might also be associated (e.g. through linkage) to lower seed production. Selection for one trait will then also select for another.
   (b) Retention of genetic diversity is particularly important in crop plants because it provides a pool of genes from which to improve strains and guard against loss of adaptability in crops. In terms of food security, it is dangerous to rely on only a restricted number of strains for most of our food. A good example is the Irish potato famine where potatoes were the main food crop and farmers relied almost exclusively on one high yielding potato variety. When this variety proved vulnerable to blight, most of the country's crop was lost and there was a huge famine. The country lost food security by relying on one variety and by not having a readily available store of diversity on which to draw.

Selective Breeding in Animals (page 185)

1. **Inbreeding** involves breeding between close relatives, and if practiced over a number of generations lead to increased homozygosity in a population. It is used by animal breeders to 'fix' desirable traits into a population, but an increase in the frequency of recessive, deleterious traits in homozygous form in a population can reduce the health and fitness and of a population and lower fertility levels. **Out-crossing** involves introducing new (unrelated) genetic material into a breeding line. It is used to increase the genetic diversity, and is used in line-breeding to restore vigour

and fertility to a breeding line.

2. Assisted reproductive technologies, such as artificial insemination, cryopreservation, embryo transfer and *in vitro* fertilisation, are used routinely to produce large numbers of offspring with desirable traits (e.g. high growth rates or superior wool production). These techniques allow the desirable traits to be fixed more quickly into the population than would be possible from traditional selective breeding techniques.

3. Positive outcomes of selective breeding in domestic animals include; desirable traits are established within a relatively short period of time, breeders are able to produce animals with high growth rates, animals can be selected for which produce high yields of meat, wool, or milk, production of animals with good temperament, improve the birthing characteristics of a breed (e.g. easy calving), produce animals specifically suited to the climate or terrain.

Negative outcomes of selective breeding include; reduction of genetic variability can make the population susceptible to disease or physiological difficulties (e.g. hip displacement), fertility may decrease, the occurrence of deleterious genes becomes more widespread and the breed loses vigour.

4. Most genetic progress in dairy herds achieved by:
   (a) Selection of (and breeding from) high quality progeny from proven stock.
   (b) Extensive use of superior sires (breeding males) through artificial insemination.

5. **Genetic gain** refers to the gain towards a (reliably attained) desirable phenotype in a breed.

6. Mixed breeds combine the best of the characteristics of both species, i.e. optimum beef and milk production.

Chloroplasts and Cell Walls (page 188)

1. Chloroplasts are primarily concentrated in the loosely packed mesophyll tissue, where there is the best access to light through the transparent, thin leaf blade. The structure of the chloroplasts themselves also aids light capture. The thylakoid membranes containing the chlorophyll, light-capturing pigment, are organised in stacks, spaced apart by lamellae to maximise efficiency of function. This arrangement maximises the amount of chlorophyll-containing membranes within the organelle.

2. (a) and (b), any two of:
   • Starch (branched carbohydrate) granules stored in amyloplasts (energy store).
   • Chloroplasts, discrete plastids containing the pigment chlorophyll, involved in photosynthesis.
   • Large vacuole, often central (vacuoles are present in animal cells, but are only small).
   • Cell wall of cellulose forming the rigid, supporting structure outside the plasma membrane.
   • Plasmodesmata.

3. A Nucleus, contains the genes for controlling cellular metabolism (all the cell's activities)

   B Cell wall supports the cell and limits its volume.

Haemoglobins (page 189)

1. (a) Respiratory pigments are able to bind reversibly with oxygen. They may bind and carry several oxygen molecules (and therefore increase the amount that can be carried over what can be dissolved in the plasma, which is very low).
   (b) The number of metal-containing prosthetic groups.

2. Organisms with a high metabolic activity (therefore high oxygen demand) have haemoglobins with a greater oxygen carrying capacity (values are highest in endothermic homeotherms, i.e. birds and mammals).

3. Large molecular weight respiratory pigments are too large to be held within cells and must be carried dissolved in the plasma.

4. Haemoglobin binds oxygen reversibly, taking up oxygen when oxygen tensions are high (lungs), carries oxygen to where it is required (the tissues) and releases it.

5. (a) As oxygen level in the blood increases, more oxygen combines with haemoglobin. However, the relationship is not linear: Hb saturation remains high even when blood oxygen levels fall very low.
   (b) When oxygen level (partial pressure) in the blood or tissues is low, haemoglobin saturation declines markedly and oxygen is released (to the tissues).

6. (a) Foetal Hb has a higher affinity for oxygen than adult Hb (it can carry 20-30% more oxygen).
   (b) This higher affinity is necessary because it enables oxygen to pass from the maternal Hb to the foetal Hb across the placenta.

7. (a) The Bohr effect
   (b) Actively respiring tissue (especially tissue with high metabolic demand, such as working muscle) consumes a lot of oxygen and generates a lot of carbon dioxide. This lowers tissue (blood) pH causing more oxygen to be released from the haemoglobin to where it is required.

8. Myoglobin preferentially picks up oxygen from Hb and is able to act as an oxygen store in the muscle.

DNA Replication (page 191)

1. DNA replication prepares a chromosome for cell division by producing two chromatids which are (or should be) identical copies of the genetic information for the chromosome.

2. (a) Step 1: Enzymes unwind DNA molecule to expose the two original strands.
   (b) Step 2: DNA polymerase enzyme uses the two original strands as templates to make complementary strands.
   (c) Step 3: The two resulting double-helix molecules coil up to form two chromatids in the chromosome.

3. (a) **Helicase**: Unwinds the 'parental' strands.
   (b) **DNA polymerase I**: Hydrolyses the RNA primer and replaces it with DNA.
   (c) **DNA polymerase III**: Elongates the leading strand. It synthesises the new Okazaki fragment until it encounters the primer on the previous fragment.
   (d) **Ligase**: Joins Okazaki fragments into a continuous length of DNA.

4. 16 minutes 40 seconds
    4 million nucleotides replicated at the rate of 4000 per
    second: 4 000 000 ÷ 4000 = 1000 s
    Convert to minutes = 1000 ÷ 60 = 16.67 minutes
    (Note that, under ideal conditions, most of a bacteria's
    cell cycle is spent in cell division).

Mitosis and the Cell Cycle (page 193)

1. A. Anaphase
    B. Prophase
    C. Late metaphase (early anaphase is also
        acceptable).
    D. Late anaphase
    E. Cytokinesis (late telophase is also acceptable).

2. Replicate the DNA to form a second chromatid.
    Coil up into visible chromosomes to avoid tangling.

3. A. Interphase: The stage between cell divisions
        (mitoses). Just before mitosis, the DNA is replicated
        to form an extra copy of each chromosome (still part
        of the same chromosome as an chromatid).
    B. Late prophase: Chromosomes condense (coil
        and fold up) into visible form. Centrioles move to
        opposite ends of the cell.
    C. Metaphase: Spindle fibers form between the
        centrioles. Chromosomes attach to the spindle
        fibers at the cell 'equator'.
    D. Late anaphase: Chromatids from each chromosome
        are pulled apart and move in opposite directions,
        towards the centrioles.
    E. Telophase: Chromosomes begin to unwind again.
        Two new nuclei form. The cell plate forms across the
        midline where the new cell wall will form.
    F. Cytokinesis: Cell cytoplasm divides to create two
        distinct 'daughter cells' from the original cell. It is in
        this form for most of its existence, and carries out its
        designated role (normal function).

The Cell Cycle and Cancer (page 195)

1. Exposure to carcinogens can damage the DNA and
    trigger uncontrolled cell division (and tumour formation).

2. A single cause of cancer can be difficult to pin-point
    because there are many factors (environmental,
    lifestyle, genetic, and ageing) which can interact and
    result in the development of a cancer.

Differentiation of Human Cells (page 196)

1. (b) Leucocyte (white blood cell)
        Various roles in the body's defence system.
    (c) Smooth muscle cell
        Responsible for muscle contraction in the gut,
        urinogenital tract, and in the walls of blood vessels.
    (d) Spermatozoon (sperm cell)
        Haploid cell carrying the genetic information of the
        male and responsible for fertilising an egg cell to
        produce a zygote (in reproduction).
    (e) Oocyte or egg cell
        Haploid cell carrying the genetic information of the
        female. It is fertilised by a sperm cell to produce a
        zygote.
    (f) Pigment cell
        Secretes the pigment melanin found in skin, hair
        and eyes which protects against sun (UV) damage.

    (g) Sensory neurone
        Nerve cells responsible for receiving and responding
        to stimuli.
    (h) Pancreatic secretory cell.
        Secretes bicarbonate ions and enzymes to aid the
        digestive process.
    (i) Skin (epithelial) cells.
        Protects underlaying tissue from mechanical and
        chemical damage, and limits pathogen entry.
        Prevent excess water loss.

2. Undifferentiated epithelial cells (e.g. cheek cells, cells
    lining the gut, skin cells) and the stem cells that give
    rise to the blood cells.

3. Depending on the destined role for the cell, different
    genes are switched on or off at different stages during
    the sequence of cell division. The cell then assumes its
    more specialised function.

Human Cell Specialisation (page 197)

1. (b) **Erythrocyte**:
        Features: Biconcave cell, lacking mitochondria,
        nucleus, and most internal membranes. Contains
        the oxygen-transporting pigment, haemoglobin.
        Role: Uptake, transport, and release of oxygen
        to the tissues. Some transport of CO_2. Lack of
        organelles creates more space for oxygen transport.
        Lack of mitochondria prevents oxygen use.
    (c) **Retinal cell**:
        Features: Long, narrow cell with light-sensitive
        pigment (rhodopsin) embedded in the membranes.
        Role: Detection of light: light causes a structural
        change in the membranes and leads to a nerve
        impulse (result is visual perception).
    (d) **Skeletal muscle cell(s)**:
        Features: Cylindrical shape with banded myofibrils.
        Capable of contraction (shortening).
        Role: Move voluntary muscles acting on skeleton.
    (e) **Intestinal epithelial cell(s)**:
        Features: Columnar cell with a high surface area as
        a result of fingerlike projections (microvilli).
        Role: Absorption of digested food.
    (f) **Motor neurone cell**:
        Features: Cell body with a long extension (the axon)
        ending in synaptic bodies. Axon is insulated with a
        sheath of fatty material (myelin).
        Role: Rapid conduction of motor nerve impulses
        from the spinal cord to effectors (e.g. muscle).
    (g) **Spermatocyte**:
        Features: Motile, flagellated cell with mitochondria.
        Nucleus forms a large proportion of the cell.
        Role: Male gamete for sexual reproduction.
        Mitochondria provide the energy for motility.
    (h) **Osteocyte**:
        Features: Cell with calcium matrix around it.
        Fingerlike extensions enable the cell to be supplied
        with nutrients and wastes to be removed.
        Role: In early stages, secretes the matrix that will be
        the structural component of bone. Provides strength.

Plant Cell Specialisation (page 198)

1. (b) **Pollen grain**:
   Features: Small, lightweight, often with spikes.
   Role: houses male gamete for sexual reproduction.
   (c) **Palisade parenchyma cell**:
   Features: Column-shaped cell with chloroplasts.
   Role: Primary photosynthetic cells of the leaf.
   (d) **Epidermal cell**:
   Features: Waxy surface on a flat-shaped cell.
   Role: Provides a barrier to water loss on leaf.
   (e) **Vessel element**:
   Features: Rigid remains of a dead cell. No cytoplasm. End walls perforated. Walls are strengthened with lignin fibres.
   Role: Rapid conduction of water through the stem. Provides support for stem/trunk.
   (f) **Stone cell**:
   Features: Very thick lignified cell wall inside the primary cell wall. The cytoplasm is restricted to a small central region of the cell.
   Role: Protection of the seed inside the fruit.
   (g) **Sieve tube member**:
   Features: Long, tube-shaped cell without a nucleus. Cytoplasm continuous with other sieve cells above and below it. Cytoplasmic streaming is evident.
   Role: Responsible for translocation of sugars etc.
   (h) **Root hair cell:**
   Features: Thin cuticle with no waxy layer. High surface area relative to volume.
   Role: Facilitates the uptake of water and ions.

Root Cell Development (page 199)

1. (a) Cells specialise to take on specific functions.
   (b) Cells are becoming longer and/or larger.
   (c) Cells are dividing by mitosis.

2. (a) Late anaphase; chromatids are being pulled apart and are at opposite poles.
   (b) Telophase; there are two new nuclei formed and the cell plate is visible.
   (c) 25 of 250 cells were in mitosis, therefore mitosis occupies 25/250 or one tenth of the cell cycle.

3. The **cambium layer** of cells (lying under the bark between the outer phloem layer of cells and the inner xylem layer of cells). **Note:** Cells dividing from each side of this layer specialise to form new phloem on the outside and new xylem on the inside.

Levels of Organisation (page 200)

1. **Animals**
   (a) **Organ system**: Nervous system, reproductive system
   (b) **Organs**: Brain, heart, spleen
   (c) **Tissues**: Blood, bone, cardiac muscle, cartilage, squamous epithelium
   (d) **Cells**: Leukocyte, mast cell, neuron, Schwann cell
   (e) **Organelles**: Lysosome, ribosomes
   (f) **Molecular**: Adrenaline, collagen, DNA, phospholipid

2. **Plants**
   (a) **Organs**: Flowers, leaf, roots
   (b) **Tissues**: Collenchyma*, mesophyll, parenchyma*, phloem, sclerenchyma
   (c) **Cells**: Companion cells, epidermal cell, fibers, tracheid
   (d) **Organelles**: Chloroplasts, ribosomes

(e) **Molecular**: Pectin, cellulose, DNA, phospholipid
* **Note**: Parenchyma and collenchyma are simple tissues comprising only one type of cell (parenchyma and collenchyma cells respectively). Simple plant tissues are usually identified by cell name alone.

Animal Tissues (page 201)

1. The organisation of cells into specialised tissues allows the tissues to perform particular functions. This improves efficiency of function because different tasks can be shared amongst specialised cells. Energy is saved in not maintaining non-essential organelles in cells that do not require them.

2. (a) **Epithelial tissues**: Single or multiple layers of simple cells forming the lining of internal and external body surfaces. Cells rest on a basement membrane of fibers and collagen and may be specialised. **Note**: epithelial cells may be variously shaped: squamous (flat), cuboidal, columnar etc.
   (b) **Nervous tissue**: Tissue comprising densely packed nerve cells specialised for transmitting electro-chemical impulses. Nerve cells may be associated with supportive cells (e.g. Schwann cells), connective tissue, and blood vessels.
   (c) **Muscle tissue**: Dense tissue comprising highly specialized contractile cells called fibers held together by connective tissues.
   (d) **Connective tissues**: Supporting tissue of the body, comprising cells widely dispersed in a semi-fluid matrix (or fluid in the case of blood and lymph).

3. (a) Muscle tissue is made up of long muscle fibre cells made up of myofibrils. The myofibrils are made up of contractile proteins actin and myosin, which cause the muscle fibres to contact when stimulated. The contraction results in movement of the organism itself (locomotion) or movement of an internal organ.
   (b) Nervous tissue comprises two main tissue types: neurones which transmit nerve signals and glial cells which provide support to the neurones. Neurones have several protrusions (dendrites or axons) from their cell body which allow conduction of nerves impulses to target cells.

Plant Tissues (page 202)

1. **Collenchyma**
   Cell type(s): collenchyma cells
   Role: provides flexible support.
   Sclerenchyma
   Cell type(s): sclerenchyma cells
   Role: provides rigid, hard support.

   Root Endodermis
   Cell type(s): endodermal cells
   Role: Provides selective barrier regulating the passage of substances from the soil to the vascular tissue.

   Pericycle
   Cell type(s): parenchyma cells
   Role: Production of branch roots, synthesis and transport of alkaloids.

   Leaf mesophyll
   Cell type(s): spongy mesophyll, palisade mesophyll
   Role: Main photosynthesis site in the plant.

Xylem
Cell type(s): tracheids, vessel members, fibers, paraenchyma cells
Role: Conducts water and dissolved minerals in vascular plants.

Phloem
Cell type(s): sieve-tube members, companion cells, parenchyma, fibers, sclereids
Role: transport of dissolved organic material (including sugars) within vascular plants.

Epidermis
Cell type(s): epidermal cells, guard cells, subsidiary cells, and epidermal hairs (trichomes).
Role: Protection against water loss, regulation of gas exchange, secretion, water and mineral absorption.

Transport and Exchange Systems (page 204)

1. Diffusion is too inefficient and slow to provide (and remove) materials (wastes, oxygen, nutrients) quickly enough to and from all the cells of larger animals. Instead, organs specialised to perform certain "exchange tasks", such as lungs and kidneys, are required and these are associated with transport mechanisms (e.g. circulatory system) to move the materials to exchange sites.

2. (a) Materials move by bulk (mass) flow in the circulatory system of a vertebrate.
   (b) Materials move by diffusion in flatworms.
   (c) Any two of: lungs or gills, gut, kidneys.

Surface Area and Volume (page 205)

1.
Cube	Surface Area	Volume	Ratio
3 cm:	$3 \times 3 \times 6 = 54$	$3 \times 3 \times 3 = 27$	2.0 to 1
4 cm:	$4 \times 4 \times 6 = 96$	$4 \times 4 \times 4 = 64$	1.5 to 1
5 cm:	$5 \times 5 \times 6 = 150$	$5 \times 5 \times 5 = 125$	1.2 to 1

2. Surface area to volume graph: see the next column:

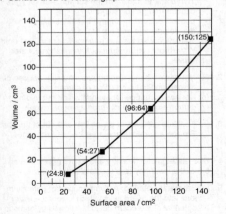

3. Volume

4. Increasing size leads to less surface area for a given volume. The surface area to volume ratio decreases.

5. Less surface area at the cell surface. This is the gas exchange surface, so large cells will have difficulty moving enough materials in and out of the cell to meet demands. This is what limits a cell's maximum size.
   Note: Eukaryote cells are typically about 0.01-0.1 mm in size, but some can be bigger than 1 mm. The largest cell is the female sex cell (ovum) of the ostrich, which averages 15-20 cm in length. Technically a single cell, it is atypical in size because almost the entire mass of the egg is food reserve in the form of yolk, which is not part of the functioning structure of the cell itself.

Gas Exchange in Animals (page 207)

1. (a) Provides adequate supply and removal of respiratory gases necessary for an active (metabolically demanding) lifestyle.
   (b) Enables animals to attain a larger size (as they are freed from a dependence on direct diffusion of gases across thin body surfaces).

2. (a) The air sacs function in ventilating the lungs (where gas exchange takes place). They facilitate one way (rather than to and fro) flow of air through the lungs.
   (b) Birds require an efficient gas exchange system because of their high metabolic rate (associated with flight). However they do not want to carry a large amount of lung tissue because this would be heavy and hinder flight (hence air sacs).

3. (a) **Body surface**
       Location: The entire body surface is involved.
       Group: Characteristic of small and/or thin animals, e.g. cnidarians, ctenophores, annelids, flatworms.
       Medium: Air (in damp environments) or water.
   (b) **Tracheal tubes**
       Location: Thin tubes extend inwards from spiracles at the body surface located on the abdomen.
       Group: Insects and some spiders.
       Medium: Air.
   (c) **Gills**
       Location: Thin, filamentous structures that extend outside the main body from behind the head/buccal area in vertebrates or associated with the thorax, abdomen or limbs in invertebrates.
       Group: Fish and most crustaceans.
       Medium: Water.
   (d) **Lungs**
       Location: Invaginations (in-pockets) of the body surface (inside body) within the thoracic region.
       Group: Vertebrates other than fish.
       Medium: Air.

4. (a) Air breathers produce mucus that keeps the gas exchange surface moist.
   (b) Some water vapour is present in lungs as a result of metabolism.

5. Large amounts of organic material clog the gill surface and prevent the water closely contacting it. Organic material also consumes a lot of oxygen in its decomposition. This reduces the amount of oxygen in the water available to animals for gas exchange.

6. An animal's gas exchange system must be appropriate to the environment in which it must operate. Gills do not function in air because the gill tissue needs to be supported by the water to prevent its collapse in the less dense medium of air. In air, the gill tissue rapidly

dries out and, once dry, the surface will not operate effectively for gas exchange. In water, lungs do not function because water is too dense a medium to enter and leave an internalised structure. The tracheae of insects operate well in terrestrial organisms of a small size because they can provide oxygen directly to the tissues. With direct oxygen delivery, a respiratory pigment in the blood is not required. In aquatic insects, the tracheae extend into flattened gills on the abdomen, and these increase oxygen uptake from the water, where oxygen extraction is more difficult than in air (because diffusion rates are slower).

Gas Exchange in Insects (page 209)

1. **Simple explanation**: In insect tracheae, gases move by diffusion directly into the tissues. Gases diffuse into and out of the fluid at the end of the tracheole, and the fluid acts as the medium for gas exchange into the tissues. **Detailed explanation**: At rest, the fluid moves into the tracheoles, oxygen diffuses into the fluid and CO_2 diffuses out. When the muscles contract, the fluid is drawn into the tissues, and oxygen can diffuse into the tissues while CO_2 diffuses out into the fluid.

2. Valves present in the spiracles control the rate of entry and exit of air into and out of the tracheal system. This enables the rate of gas exchange to be regulated according to the changing activity levels (and therefore gas exchange requirements) of the insect.

3. Ventilation occurs when the insect makes rhythmic body movements helping to move the air in and out of the tracheae.

4. Tracheal systems provide direct delivery of oxygen to the tissues, without relying on a circulatory fluid combined with a respiratory pigment. This system is rapid and efficient for small sized organisms and has the advantage of reducing the reliance of insects on water (water is a necessity for organisms relying on diffusion across a moist body surface). A reduced dependence on freely available water has allowed insects to colonise some of the driest, most inhospitable places on Earth.

Gas Exchange in Freshwater (page 210)

1. (a)-(c) any of, in any order:
   – Tracheal gills increase surface area for gas exchange, e.g. aquatic insect larvae such as mayfly larvae. Note that the anal and caudal "gills" of some aquatic insects are often involved in osmoregulation.
   – Trapped air beneath the wings provides an oxygen store above the spiracles, e.g. *Dytiscus*.
   – A plastron formed by a layer of air trapped against the spiracles by hydrofuge hairs. A plastron forms a non-compressible gill into which gases can diffuse, e.g. adult hydrophilid beetles.
   – Siphons to the water surface provide a link between the spiracles and the air above, e.g. mosquito larvae.

2. Physiological adaptation: Presence of a respiratory pigment (haemoglobin) either in the blood (*Chironomus*) or in the abdomen (*Anisops*).

Gas Exchange in Fish (page 211)

1. (a)-(c) any of, in any order:
   – Greatly folded surface of gills (high surface area).
   – Gills supported and kept apart from each other by the gas exchange medium (water).
   – Water flow across the gill surface is opposite to that of the blood flow in the gill capillaries (countercurrent), facilitating oxygen uptake.
   – Pumping mechanism of operculum aids movement of the water across the gas exchange surface.

2. (a) As blood flows through the gill capillaries (gaining oxygen) it encounters blood of increasing oxygen content, so a diffusion gradient is maintained across the entire gill surface.
   (b) Parallel flow would result in rapid equilibration of oxygen saturation between the blood and the water and diffusion into the blood would stop.

3. (a) **Ventilation**: Moving water across the gill surface.
   (b) Ventilation prevents stagnation of the water at the gill surface and maintains the concentration gradient necessary for continued gas exchange.
   (c) **Pumping**: Operculum acts as a pump, drawing water past the gill filaments.
   Continuous swimming: Continuous (usually rapid) swimming with the mouth open produces a constant flow of water over the gill filaments.
   (d) These fish rely on being able to swim rapidly and continuously to provide the necessary ventilation of their gill surfaces. If they do not have the room to do this they will asphyxiate and die.

4. Oxygen availability in water is low anyway, so anything that lowers this still further (high temperature of decomposition of organic material) increases the vulnerability of fish to oxygen deprivation. This is especially so for fish with high oxygen requirements such as trout and salmon.

Stomata and Gas Exchange (page 213)

1. (a) and (b) Any two of:
   – Thin blade to maximise the surface area for light capture and gas exchanges.
   – Loosely packed mesophyll facilitates gas movements into and out of the leaf.
   – Transparent so there is no impairment to light entry.
   – Waterproof cuticle reduces transpirational water losses.

2. (a) Net gas exchange (no photosynthesis): net use of oxygen and net production of carbon dioxide.
   (b) Net gas exchange (photosynthesis): net use of carbon dioxide and net production of oxygen.

3. (a) Facilitate diffusion of gases into and out of the leaf.
   (b) Provide a large surface area for gas exchanges (around the cell.

4. Stomata regulate the entry and exit of gases into and out of the leaf (they also regulate water loss).

5. (a) **Stomatal opening**: Active transport of potassium ions into the guard cells (which lowers the water potential of the guard cells) is followed by osmotic influx of water. This causes the guard cells to swell and become turgid. The structure of the guard cell walls causes them to buckle out, opening the stoma.
   (b) **Stomatal closure**: Potassium ions leave the guard

cell (making the water potential of the guard cells less negative) and water follows by osmosis. The guard cells become flaccid and sag together closing the stoma.

Adaptations of Xerophytes (page 215)

1. **Xeromorphic** adaptations allow xerophytes to survive and grow in areas with low or irregular water supplies.

2. (a)-(c), three in any order:
   - Modification of leaves to reduce transpirational loss (e.g. spines, curling, leaf hairs).
   - Shallow, but extensive fibrous root system to extend area from which water is taken and to take advantage of overnight condensation.
   - Water storage in stems or leaves.
   - Rounded, squat shape of plant body to reduce surface area for water loss.

3. The CAM metabolism (found only in xerophytic plants, many of which are succulents) allows carbon dioxide to be fixed during the dark. This produces organic acids which accumulate in the leaves and later release carbon dioxide into the Calvin cycle during daylight (when light energy is available to provide H⁺ and ATP for photosynthesis). The stomata can then stay closed during the day when transpirational losses are highest.

4. A moist microenvironment reduces the gradient in water potential between the leaf and the air, so there is less tendency for water to leave the plant.

5. In a high salt environment, free water is scarce. Sea shoreline plants (halophytes) therefore have many xeromorphic adaptations.

Mammalian Transport (page 217)

1. (a) Head (d) Gut (intestines)
   (b) Lungs (e) Kidneys
   (c) Liver (f) Genitals/lower body

Arteries (page 218)

1. (a) Tunica externa (c) Endothelium
   (b) Tunica media (d) Blood (or lumen)

2. (a) Thick, elastic walls can withstand the high pressure of the blood being pumped from the heart. **Note**: Elasticity also helps to even out the surges that occur with each contraction of the heart. This keeps the blood moving forward in a continuous flow.
   (b) Blood pressure is low within the arterioles.

3. The smooth muscle around arteries helps to regulate blood flow and pressure. By contracting or relaxing it alters the diameter of the artery and adjusts the volume of blood as required.

4. (a) The diameter of the artery increases.
   (b) The blood pressure decreases.

Capillaries and Tissue Fluid (page 219)

1. **Capillaries** are very small blood vessels forming networks or beds that penetrate all parts of the body. The only tissue present is an endothelium of squamous epithelial cells. In contrast, **arteries** have a

thin endothelium, a central layer of elastic tissue and smooth muscle and a thick outer layer of elastic and connective tissue. **Veins** have a thin endothelium, a central layer of elastic and muscle tissue and a thin outer layer of elastic connective tissue. In addition, veins also have valves.

2. (a) Sinusoids differ from capillaries in that they are wider and follow a more convoluted path through the tissue. They are lined with phagocytic cells rather than the usual endothelial lining of capillaries.
   (b) Capillaries and sinusoids are similar in that they both transport blood from arterioles to venules.

3. (a) Leakage of fluid from capillaries produces tissue fluid, which bathes the tissues, providing oxygen and nutrients as well as a medium for the transport (away) of metabolic wastes, e.g. CO_2.
   (b) Capillary walls are thin enough to allow exchanges. No exchange occurs in arteries and veins because the walls of arteries and veins are too thick.

4. (a) Arteriolar end: Hydrostatic pressure predominates in causing fluid to move out of the capillaries.
   (b) Venous end: Increased concentration of solutes and reduction in hydrostatic pressure at the venous end of a capillary bed **lowers the solute potential** within the capillary and there is a tendency for water and solutes to re-enter the capillary.

5. (a) Most tissue fluid finds it way directly back into the capillaries as a result of net inward pressure at the venule end of the capillary bed.
   (b) The lymph vessels (which parallel the blood system) drain tissue fluid (as lymph) back into the heart, thereby returning it into the main circulation.

Veins (page 221)

1. (a) Veins have less elastic and muscle tissue than arteries.
   (b) Veins have a larger lumen than arteries.

2. Most of the structural differences between arteries and veins are related to the different blood pressures inside the vessels. Blood in veins travels at low pressure and veins do not need to be as strong, hence the thinner layers of muscle and elastic tissue and the relatively larger lumen. **Note**: There is still enough elastic and muscle tissue to enable the veins to adjust to changes in blood volume and pressure.

3. Veins are "massaged" by the skeletal muscles (e.g. leg muscles). Valves (together with these muscular movements) help to return venous blood to the heart by preventing backflow away from the heart. **Note**: When skeletal muscles contract and tighten around a vein the valves open and blood is driven towards the heart. When the muscles relax, the valves close, preventing backflow.

4. Venous blood oozes out in an even flow from a wound because it has lost a lot of pressure after passing through the narrow capillary vessels (with their high resistance to flow). Arterial blood spurts out rapidly because it is being pumped directly from the heart and has not yet entered the capillary networks.

Root Structure (page 222)

1. Any three of the following:
   - Roots anchor the plant into the soil
   - Absorb water and inorganic nutrients from the soil.
   - Sites for production of hormones gibberellins and cytokinins, which influence growth and development.
   - Specialised roots can have a variety of roles including supporting stems (prop roots), or supplying oxygen to underwater roots (pneumatophores) in the case of mangroves.

2. (a) and (b), any two of:
   - The primary xylem forms a star shape in the root centre (with usually 3 or 4 points).
   - The vascular tissue forms a central cylinder through the root (stele).
   - The stele is surrounded by a pericycle.

3. **Root hairs** increase the surface area for absorption.

4. The endodermis comprises a single layer of cells with a waterproof suberin coating along two sides. This waterproofing forces water to flow in one direction, into the vascular cylinder, rather than into the cortex.

Transpiration (page 223)

1. (a) They take up water by the roots.
   (b) Any of:
      - Transpiration stream enables plants to absorb sufficient quantities of the minerals they need (the minerals are absorbed with the water and are often in low concentration in the soil).
      - Transpiration helps cool the plant.

2. Water moves by osmosis in all cases. In any order:
   (a) **Transpiration pull**: Photosynthesis and evaporative loss of water from leaf surfaces create a more negative water potential in the leaf cells than elsewhere in the plant, facilitating movement of water along a gradient in water potential towards the site of evaporation (stomata).
   (b) **Capillary effect/cohesion-adhesion**: Water molecules cling together and adhere to the xylem, creating an unbroken water column through the plant. The upward pull on the sap creates a tension that facilitates movement of water up the plant.
   (c) **Root pressure** provides a weak push effect for upward water movement.

3. (a)-(c) any of the following: High wind, high light, high temperature, low humidity. All increase the rate of evaporation from the leaves.

4. The system excludes air. As the plant loses water through transpiration, it takes up water from the flask via roots (or cut stem). The volume removed from the flask by the plant is withdrawn from the pipette; this can be measured on the pipette graduations.

5. (a) Measurements were taken at the start and at the end of the experiment in the same conditions (still air, light shade, 20°C). These rates should be the same (give or take experimental error). This indicates that the plant has not been damaged by the experiment and any results are therefore a real response to the experimental conditions.
   (b) Moving air and bright sunlight increase transpiration rate, because they increase the rate of evaporation from the leaves. **Note**: Lower humidity could

also be said to increase transpiration rate (by increasing the gradient in water potential), but this would need to be tested further, i.e. the results here do not conclusively show this. Another test where the effects of darkness and humidity level were separated would be required. This is a good discussion point for students investigating experimental design and interpretation of results.

(c) Still, humid conditions reduce evaporative loss, dark conditions stop photosynthetic production of sugars (therefore solute concentration in the leaves falls). Both these reduce transpiration rate by reducing the concentration gradient for water movement.

Uptake at the Root (page 225)

1. (a) Passive absorption of minerals along with the water and active transport.
   (b) Apoplastic pathway (about 90%): Moving through the spaces within the cellulose cell wall.
   Symplastic pathway: Moving through the cell cytoplasm from cell to cell via plasmodesmata.

2. Large water uptake allows plants to take up sufficient quantities of minerals from the soil. These are often in very low concentration in the soil and low water uptakes would not provide adequate quantities.

3. (a) The **casparian strip** represents a waterproof barrier to water flow through the apoplastic pathway into the stele. It forces the water to move into the cells (i.e. move via the symplastic route).
   (b) This feature enables the plant to better regulate its uptake of ions, i.e. take up ions selectively. The movement of ions through the apoplast cannot be regulated because the flow does not occur across any partially permeable membranes.

The New Tree of Life (page 227)

1. The argument for the new classification as three domains is based on the fact that the genetic differences between the Bacteria and the Archaea are at least as great as between the Eukarya and the Bacteria. In other words, the traditional scheme does not accurately reflect the true evolutionary (genetic) relationship between the three groupings.

2. Any one of:
   - The eukaryote groups are given much less prominence, reflecting the true diversity of the prokaryote groups.
   - The Archaea have been separated out as distinct from other bacteria in order to reflect their uniqueness and indicate their true relationship to eukaryotes and to other prokaryotes.

3. The six kingdom classification scheme splits the prokaryotes into the kingdoms Eubacteria and Archaebacteria. These taxa are the same two domains that the three domain classification system uses.

The Species Concept (page 228)

1. Behavioural (they show no interest in each other).

2. Physical barrier; sea separating Australia from SE Asia.

3. The red wolf is rare and may have difficulty finding

another member of its species to mate with.

4. The populations on the two land masses, which have identical appearance and habitat requirements, were connected relatively recently by a land bridge during the last ice age (about 18 000 years ago). This would have permitted breeding between the populations. Individuals from the current populations have been brought together and are able to interbreed and produce fertile offspring.

Behaviour and Species Recognition (page 229)

1. (a) **Courtship** behaviour is a means of assessing the suitability, quality, and readiness of a mate and an effective way of ensuring reproductive isolation. it also has a role in reducing natural intraspecific aggression in the potential mate.
   (b) Stereotypical behaviors are easily recognised and will elicit appropriate (and equally recognisable) behaviours in the prospective mate.

2. Effective courtship provides a way to ensure that species do not mistakenly waste resources by mating with another species. This helps to ensure the production of viable offspring and maintains the integrity of the species gene pool.

DNA and Taxonomy (page 230)

1. (a) Morphology recognises the importance of physical features in distinguishing between groups of organisms (it is a simpler and more familiar operation). It also recognises the amount of morphological change that occurs in species after their divergence from a common ancestor.
   (b) Biochemical evidence produces phylogenies that more correctly represent the true evolutionary relationships between groups (taxa). **Note:** The phylogenies produced this way may be more difficult to interpret and apply and may not recognise morphological changes occurring after divergence from a common ancestor.

2. Biochemical evidence compares DNA and proteins between species and provides a more direct measure of common inheritance. **Teacher's note:** For some species, biochemical evidence has shown that earlier phylogenies were in error. Sometimes (as in the case of primates) the earlier phylogenies reflected the human view of their own position in the phylogeny. Morphological similarities can arise through convergent evolution in unrelated groups. Biochemical evidence is not clouded by this type of adaptive morphology.

3. (a) Pongidae   (b) Hominidae

Classification System (page 231)

1. (a) 1. Kingdom   (b) 1. Animal
       2. Phylum   2. Chordata
       3. Class   3. Mammalia
       4. Order   4. Primates
       5. Family   5. Hominidae
       6. Genus   6. *Homo*
       7. Species   7. *sapiens*

2. A two part naming system where the first word

(capitalised and italicised) denotes the genus and the second word (lower case and italicised) denotes the species. Sometimes a third word (also lower case and italicised) denotes a subspecies.

3. (a) and (b) in any order:
   Avoid confusion over the use of common names for organisms; provide a unique name for each type of organism; attempt to determine/define the evolutionary relationship of organisms (phylogeny).

4. Any of the following:
   DNA profiling/sequencing: Where the unique genetic makeup of an individual is revealed and used for comparisons with related organisms.
   DNA hybridisation: Where the percentage DNA similarity between organisms is compared.
   Amino acid sequencing: Where the number of amino acid differences between organisms are compared.
   Immunological distance: Indirectly estimate the degree of similarity of proteins in different species.

5. (a) **Monotreme:** Egg laying with little internal development before laying, most development takes place in the egg
   (b) **Marsupial:** Birth takes place after limited internal development. Most development occurs after 'foetus' moves to the pouch and attaches to the nipple.
   (c) **Placental:** Long period of internal development, sustained by placenta. Birth takes place at highly developed stage.

DNA Hybridisation (page 233)

1. The similarity of DNA from different species can be established in a rudimentary way by measuring how closely single strands from each species mesh together. The more similar the DNA, the harder it is to separate them.

2. Molecular evidence, especially based on highly conserved sequences, may be more accurate than classifications based solely on morphology because: (1) it is more objective than morphological determinations and (2) it is independent of coevolutionary influences. Plants with particular niche requirements often have similar morphological adaptations that are the result of coevolution and not shared ancestry, and these may cause them to be grouped together. The use of molecular evidence avoids the confusion potentially posed by adaptation and emphasises the most parsimonious (least complicated) phylogeny as is required by modern biological systematics.

Immunological Studies (page 234)

1. **Immunological studies** have been used as a crude means of determining the similarity of proteins between species. The technique uses the ability of the immune system of a mammal to recognise foreign proteins. Results have confirmed schemes of evolutionary relationships based on anatomical evidence.

2. (a) 60   (b) 25 – 30

3. Distantly related (branched off 35-40 million years ago).

4. 25 million years ago.

Protein Comparisons (page 235)

1. Chimpanzees have identical amino acid sequences to humans for some proteins, while gorillas vary only slightly. Other primates, such as monkeys, have many more differences in the chemical makeup of their proteins.

2. (a) Respiratory proteins are highly conserved because of their crucial role in the respiratory pathway. Most changes are likely to be deleterious so they tend to change very little over evolutionary time.
   (b) Such proteins are good candidates for use in establishing homologies because the few changes that are retained through time are likely to be meaningful, i.e. represent major divergences in evolutionary lines.

3. Protein homologies require that the molecular clock data (the rate of molecular change over time) be calibrated against material evidence, such as fossil evidence, before firm conclusions can be based on them. Other problems can relate to the evolving functions of the encoded protein and differences in the rate at which the clock runs in different species (e.g. with longer generation times etc).

Antibiotics (page 237)

1. Inhibiting cell wall production prevents cell division, which effectively halts the growth of the bacterial population.

2. Using a broad-spectrum drug to treat an unidentified bacterial infection can be advantageous in some cases as valuable time can be saved in treating the infection. However, with use of a broad-spectrum drug, much of the body's normal microbial flora of the body is also removed. The body's normal flora usually competes with and checks the growth of potential pathogens and other microbes. When it is removed, the risk of infections from opportunistic pathogens, such as fungi, is increased. In addition, even a broad-spectrum drug may not prove maximally effective against the target pathogen.

3. Ideally, an antimicrobial drug should have selective toxicity, targeting and killing the pathogen without harming the host. There is a wide range of antibiotics available; broad spectrum antibiotics, effective against a wide range of bacteria, are useful when the identity of the pathogen is unknown and a treatment decision must be made quickly. Narrow spectrum antibiotics are useful when the pathogen is known and can be targeted directly. The latter are the preferred choice as they limit the disturbance to the body's own microbial flora. Some patients exhibit side effects, ranging from discomfort to anaphylaxis, but the vast majority of people experience few difficulties with their use.

Evolution of Drug Resistance (page 238)

1. Antibiotic resistance refers to the resistance bacteria show to antibiotics that would normally inhibit their growth. In other words, they no longer show a reduction in growth response in the presence of the antibiotic.

2. (a) Antibiotic resistance arises in a bacterial population as result of mutation. Some bacteria

can also acquire these changes in DNA (conferring resistance) by transfer of genes between bacteria by conjugation (horizontal evolution).
   (b) Resistance can become widespread as a result of (1) transfer of genetic material between bacteria (horizontal evolution) or by (2) increasing resistance with each generation a result of natural selection processes (vertical evolution). In the latter case, the antibiotic provides the environment in which selection for resistance can take place. It is exacerbated by overuse and misuse of antibiotics.

3. Widespread antibiotic resistance has implications for the treatment and control of what have been, in the past, quite easily treated diseases. Tuberculosis is one good example. Historically, it was effectively treated with antibiotics, but complacency over its control has lead to increasing multiple drug resistance in the *Mtb* population and a resurgence in the number of TB cases. This has huge implications for public health because more people live with (resistant forms of) the disease and spread it to more people as a result. In addition, the costs associated with treating TB are now also much higher.

   In general, increasing resistance increases the costs lowers the efficacy of treating disease.

The Basis of Resistance (page 239)

1. Horizontal gene transmission describes the transfer of genetic material directly between bacteria by conjugation, transduction, or transformation. Vertical gene transmission describes the passing of genetic information from generation to generation by cell division.

2. When bacteria acquire several different mechanisms of resistance there is a much greater chance that they will become resistant to different classes of antibiotics. If this occurs, the treatment options against that particular pathogen are greatly reduced.

Global Biodiversity (page 240)

1. Species diversity refers to the number of different species within an area (species richness), while genetic diversity describes the diversity of genes within a particular species. Biodiversity is defined as the measure of all genes, species, and ecosystems in a region, so both genetic and species diversity are important in determining a region's total biodiversity.

2. Consideration of ecosystem diversity is very important when considering areas to set aside for conservation purposes because regions with diverse ecosystems will have higher levels of species richness, and the two measures are interdependent. A loss of habitat diversity will have a negative impact on the species richness of an area, and habitat diversity itself is contingent on species richness. Loss or decline in one will invariably result in loss or decline in the other.

3. The hotspot list is as follows:

1 **Tropical Andes**
The richest and most diverse hotspot where it is home to 20 000 endemic plants and at least 1500 endemic

non-fish vertebrates.

2 Sundaland
Some of the largest islands in the world are found here in Southeast Asia. The second-richest hotspot in endemic plants, and well known for its mammalian fauna, which includes the orangutan.

3 Mediterranean basin
The site of many ancient and modern civilisations, it is the archetype and largest of the five Mediterranean-climate hotspots (also see nos. 9, 12, 19 and 22). One of the hotspots most heavily affected by human activity, it has 13 000 endemic plants, and is home to a number of interesting vertebrates such as the Spanish ibex.

4 Madagascar and Indian Ocean islands
Madagascar is a top conservation priority as this 'mini-continent' has undergone extensive deforestation. This hotspot is famous for reptiles such as chameleons and is home to all the world's lemur species.

5 Indo-Burma
An area stretching from the eastern slopes of the Himalayas through Burma and Thailand to Indochina. This region hosts the world's highest freshwater turtle diversity (43 species), and a diverse array of mammals. Several new ungulate species, such as the saola and giant muntjac, were recently discovered here.

6 Caribbean
One of the highest concentrations of species per unit area on Earth. Reptiles are particularly diverse (497 species are found here), 80 percent of which are found nowhere else. Non-fish vertebrates number 1518.

7 Atlantic Forest region
Once covering an area nearly three times the size of California, the Atlantic Forest has been reduced to about 7% of its original extent. It is most famous for 25 different kinds of primates, 20 of which are endemic. Among its best-known 'flagship species' are the critically endangered muriquis and lion tamarins.

8 Philippines
The most devastated of the hotspots, the forest cover has been reduced to 3% of its original extent. The Philippines is especially rich in endemic mammals and birds, such as the Philippine eagle.

9 Cape Floristic Province
This Mediterranean-type hotspot in southern Africa covers an area roughly the size of Ireland, and is now approximately 20% of its original extent. It is home to 8200 plant species, more than 5500 of which are endemic.

10 Mesoamerica
Forming a land bridge between two American continents, this hotspot features species representative of North and South America as well as its own unique biota. The spider and howler monkeys, Baird's tapir and unusual horned guan are 'flagship species'.

11 Brazilian Cerrado
A vast area of savanna and dry forest, the Cerrado is Brazil's new agricultural frontier and has been greatly altered by human activity in the past few decades. Home to 4400 endemic plants and several well-known mammal species, including the giant anteater, Brazilian tapir, and maned wolf.

12 Southwest Australia
A Mediterranean-type system, this hotspot is rich in endemic plants, reptiles, and marsupials including numbat, honey possum and quokka. It is also home to some of the world's tallest trees, e.g. giant eucalyptus.

13 Mountains of South-Central China
An area of extreme topography, these mountains are home to several of the world's best-known mammals, including the giant panda, the red panda, and the golden monkey. This hotspot is largely unexplored and may hold many undiscovered species.

14 Polynesia/Micronesia
This hotspot comprises thousands of tiny islands scattered over the vast Pacific, from Fiji and Hawaii to Easter Island and is noteworthy for its land snails, birds, and reptiles. Hawaii has suffered some of the most severe extinctions in modern history, due in part to the introduction of non-native plant and animal species.

15 New Caledonia
One of the smallest hotspots yet it has the largest concentration of unique plants with five plant families found nowhere else on Earth. This hotspot also features many endemic birds, such as the kagu, a long-legged, flightless forest dweller representing an entire family.

16 Choco-Darien Western Ecuador
Some of the world's wettest rain forests are found here, and amphibians, plants and birds are particularly abundant. It has one of the highest levels of endemism of any hotspot with 210 endemic amphibian species of the 350 species found here.

17 Guinean Forests of West Africa
(in error, this hotspot was not numbered on the map). With the highest mammalian diversity of any hotspot, these forests are home to the rare pygmy hippopotamus and many other striking species, including the western chimpanzee, Diana monkey and several forest duikers. The numbers of these endemic mammals have been severely reduced by large-scale logging and hunting.

18 Western Ghats/Sri Lanka
The Western Ghats mountain chain and adjacent island of Sri Lanka harbour high concentrations of endemic reptiles; of 259 reptile species, 161 are found nowhere else on Earth. This hotspot is also home to a number of 'flagship species', including the lion-tailed macaque.

19 California Floristic Province
Extending along the coast of California and into Oregon and northwestern Baja California, Mexico, this is one of five hotspots featuring a Mediterranean-type climate of hot, dry summers and cool, wet winters. It is especially rich in plants, with more than 4000 plant species, almost half of which are endemic.

20 Succulent Karoo
The only arid hotspot, the Succulent Karoo of southern Africa is renowned for unique succulent plants, as well as lizards and tortoises. In Namaqualand, in the southern part of this hotspot, a seasonal burst of bloom in September attracts many tourists.

21 New Zealand
This hotspot claims a number of world-famous endemic bird species, including kiwi (a nocturnal, flightless bird), takahe (a diurnal, flightless bird), and the critically endangered kakapo (a large, flightless parrot).

22 Central Chile
This hotspot features an arid region as well as a more typical Mediterranean-type zone. Best known for its incredible variety of plant species but also features unusual fauna, including one of the largest birds in the Americas, the Andean condor.

23 Caucasus
Situated between the Black Sea and the Caspian Sea, Caucasus habitats range from temperate forests to grasslands. A diversity of plants have been recorded here with some 6300 species, more than 1600 of which are endemic.

24 Wallacea
Named for the 19th century naturalist Alfred Russel Wallace, this hotspot comprises the large Indonesian island of Sulawesi, the Moluccas and many smaller islands. The area is particularly rich in endemic mammals and birds.

25 Eastern Arc Mountains/ Coastal Forests of Tanzania and Kenya
A chain of upland and coastal forests, this hotspot claims one of the densest concentrations of endemic plant and primate species in the world. It is home to African violets and 4000 other plant species, as well as the 1500 remaining Kirk's red colobus monkeys.

Britain's Biodiversity (page 241)

1. Table and graph below:

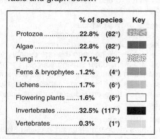

	% of species	Key
Protozoa	22.8% (82°)	
Algae	22.8% (82°)	
Fungi	17.1% (62°)	
Ferns & bryophytes	1.2% (4°)	
Lichens	1.7% (6°)	
Flowering plants	1.6% (6°)	
Invertebrates	32.5% (117°)	
Vertebrates	0.3% (1°)	

Proportion of British species in different taxonomic groups
0.3%

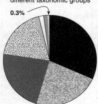

2. Invertebrate phyla, protozoans, algae, and lower plants show a much higher biodiversity (as measured by number of identified species) than the higher plants and vertebrate taxa.

3. (a) Our knowledge of the biodiversity (as measured by number of identified species) of invertebrate animals and bacteria (especially the latter) is poor compared with that of vertebrates i.e. there are many more undescribed species, and there is considerable doubt as to how many species actually exist.

(b) Vertebrates are large, conspicuous organisms with (for the most part) sexual reproduction. This makes determination of "a species" relatively simple even if morphology is similar. **Note**: Many invertebrates and bacteria are as yet undescribed and there is much doubt as to what constitutes a species in those organisms that rarely reproduce sexually. This is especially the case for bacteria, where species classification tends to based upon criteria other than the ability to interbreed. For invertebrates that normally reproduce by parthenogenesis, identification of type specimens (specimens representing the species) is particularly difficult. Morphology may be very similar between different species and species distinction may be based only on physiological or genetic criteria.

4. The UK has a low level of endemism. It is not far from the European continent ; this facilitates species transfers. In addition, its isolation from the continental land mass has been limited for much of its geologic history (isolation is required for endemism to develop).

5. (a) 12 000 − 3800 = 8200
8200 ÷ 12 000 X 100 = 68.3%. Nearly 70% decline.

(b) The barn owl is widely distributed, so the population does not have the problems associated with scattered or isolated distribution. The causes of decline have been identifiable and manageable in that rather simple measures can be taken to increase survival rates of both the young and breeding adults. They are also relatively adaptable birds, taking a variety of prey and responding well to habitat enhancement (e.g. using new nest sites).

Loss of Biodiversity (page 243)

1. Loss of biodiversity from an ecosystem has a cascade effect to the remaining species. The effects depend very much on the species that disappears (e.g. predator, producer) but, in general, species loss results in altered food chains and food webs, allowing for the proliferation of some species and the demise of others. Other changes include a loss of stability and resilience, and disruption to normal processes, interactions and outcomes, such as nutrient cycling, soil formation, pollination, oxygen production, carbon sequestration and climate regulation.

Tropical Deforestation (page 244)

1. (a) They enhance removal of carbon dioxide from the atmosphere (anti-greenhouse).

(b) They maintain species diversity.

(c) They have, as-yet-undiscovered, potentially useful species for medicines etc.

2. Tropical deforestation has three primary causes: Logging, fires, and road-building (associated with clearance for agriculture). Logging and fires destroy forest. Intrusion of roads into pristine forested areas allows the invasion of weed species, increases erosion, and prevents the reestablishment of forest species. Agriculture maintains cleared areas and prevents forest reestablishment. Lengthy continued agriculture on thin tropical soils precludes the easy reestablishment of

forest once the agricultural land has been abandoned.

Agriculture and Diversity (page 245)

1. (a) Advantage 1: High yields are maintained by intensive farming even though some areas are retired from production.
   (b) Advantage 2: There is a financial incentive if certain areas are left as conservation estate (income from tourism related to conservation areas and direct compensation for loss of income from land turned over to conservation).
   (c) Disadvantage: Intensive farming practices may have a lasting detrimental impact on surrounding conservation estate. The financial rewards of conserving land may not compensate for the income lost through having unproductive land.

2. (a) and (b) any advantages of:
   – Hedgerows provide habitat and food for wildlife.
   – Hedgerows act as corridors along which animals can move between regions of suitable habitat (e.g. for feeding). Corridors are also important for the establishment and expansion of some plant species.
   – Hedgerows provide habitat for the predators of prey species. This may also benefit the farmer by helping to keep pest species under control.

3. (a) and (b) any disadvantages of:
   – Hedgerows hamper effective use of some farm machinery.
   – Hedgerows take up space that could otherwise be used for grazing or crop production.
   – Hedgerows provide habitat for competitors to grazing livestock (e.g. hares) and predators (foxes).

4. (a) Habitat loss (hedgerows and woodland areas).
   (b) Decline in abundance and diversity of food sources associated with habitat loss.

5. (a)
   – Hedgerow legislation to preserve existing hedgerow habitats.
   – Policies to preserve or restore woodland cover in previously wooded areas (afforestation).
   – Schemes (with financial incentives) to encourage environmentally sensitive farming practices.
   (b) Biodiversity estimates would determine the biodiversity levels in certain habitats (e.g. with hedgerows or without). This would identify areas which required implementation of the biodiversity policies mentioned above, and also provide a baseline to measure the effectiveness of the strategies once implemented.

Measuring Diversity (page 247)

1. (a) **Species richness** measures the number of species within an ecosystem, whereas **species evenness** describes how equally the species are distributed within an ecosystem.
   (b) Both measures are important when considering species conservation. Species richness could give an indication of ecosystem stability, and therefore how at-risk particular species may be. Species evenness provides an indication of the species distribution (a limited distribution or a distribution

where individuals are widely separated may indicate the species is at risk).

2. Sampling must be carried out in an unbiased manner which provides a true representation of the ecosystem. This is usually achieved by random sampling techniques. The sample size must be large enough to gather a true representation of the species present, and the sampling method used must be suitable for capturing information of the species likely to be present.

3. High diversity systems have a greater number of biotic interactions operating to buffer them against change (the loss or decline of one component (species) is less likely to affect the entire ecosystem). With a large number of species involved, ecosystem processes, such as nutrient recycling, are more efficient and less inclined to disruption.

4. **Keystone species** are pivotal to some important ecosystem function such as production of biomass or nutrient recycling. Because their role is disproportionately large, their removal has a similarly disproportionate effect on ecosystem function.

5. Species diversity index used in (any of):
   – Comparisons of similar ecosystems which have been subjected to (beneficial or detrimental) human influence (e.g. restoration or pollution).
   – Assessment of the same ecosystem before and after some event (fire, flood, pollution, environmental restoration).
   – Assessment of the same ecosystem along some environmental gradient (e.g. distance from a point source of pollution).
   – Assessment of the biodiversity value of an area for the purposes of management or preservation (tends to be a political lobbying point).

6. (a) DI = 37 x 36 ÷ ((7 x 6) + (10 x 9) + (11 x 10) + (2 x 1) + (4 x 3) + (3 x 2)) = 1332 ÷ 262 = 5.08
   (b) Without any frame of reference (e.g. for a known high or low diversity system), no reasonable comment can be made about the diversity of this ecosystem. Herein lies the problem with an index that has no theoretical upper boundary.

NOTES